Directory of Directories
on the Internet

Directory of Directories on the Internet

on the Internet

A Guide to Information Sources

Gregory B. Newby

Mecklermedia

Westport · London

Library of Congress Cataloging-in-Publication Data

Newby, Gregory B.
    Directory of directories on the Internet : a guide to information
sources / Gregory B. Newby.
        p. cm.
    Includes bibliographical references and indexes.
    ISBN 0-88736-768-2 (alk. paper) : $
    1. Internet (Computer Network)--Directories. I. Title.
TK5105.875.I57N49   1994
384.3'3--dc20   93-29278
                                                        CIP

British Library Cataloguing-in-Publication Data

Newby, Gregory
    Directory of Directories on the Internet:
    Guide to Information Sources
    I. Title
    004.6

    ISBN 0-88736-768-2

Second Printing, February 1994

Mecklermedia, 11 Ferry Lane West, Westport, CT 06880.
Mecklermedia Ltd., Artillery House, Artillery Row, London SW1P 1RT, UK.

Printed on acid free paper.
Printed and bound in the United States of America.

Contents

Chapter 1: Introduction

The Internet is growing rapidly, and tools are needed to be able to use it to maximum advantage.

Chapter 2: Tools for Networked Information Discovery and Retrieval

This chapter describes in detail tools that are useful for finding information via the Internet. As the Internet grows, these tools will play a more dominant role in getting you to where you want to go.

Chapter 3: Resource Guides

Various directories and guides strive to serve as a general introduction or manual for network use. This section lists these materials.

Chapter 4: OPACs

"Online Public Access Catalogs" (OPACs) refers minimally to the computerized card catalog of a library. Many libraries offer additional services.

Chapter 5: E-mail, Mailing Lists, and Newsgroups

This chapter presents methods for getting in touch with individuals and groups. First is how to find a specific person's E-mail address. Second is how to find out about an electronic mailing list for a particular topic. Third is how to find out about what Usenet newsgroups are available on various topics. Finally, a resource for identifying electronic journals and newsletters is described.

Chapter 6: Resources for Anyone

This chapter lists various resources which are useful for almost anyone.

Chapter 7: FTP Directories

Anonymous FTP is still one of the best ways to get data, resources, software, archives, and many other things. Finding the right place to FTP to is not always easy, though: Archie is useful, but doesn't facilitate topical browsing. This chapter gives brief summaries of the holdings of some of the most useful sites for Anonymous FTP on the Internet.

Chapter 8: Special Interest and Regional Resources

Many academic and professional fields or areas of interest are served by a number of mailing lists, newsgroups, or other information resources. This chapter includes resources for various fields, areas of study, or geographic locations.

Chapter 9: Individual Efforts

Almost all of the available Internet resources were created by individuals or small groups. This chapter includes some resources which are best identified with their producer.

Chapter 10: Books

There are a number of books for pointing the way towards the Internet. This chapter includes a brief description of each.

Chapter 11: Miscellaneous

The variety in this chapter reflects nicely the variety on the Internet.

Chapter 12: Keeping Informed of Future Directions

Appendices:

Indexes

Preface

One problem that I faced in writing this book was defining the term "directory" for the purpose of delimiting what would be included. Luckily, I did not allow this problem to keep me up nights. Even without consulting a dictionary, I decided that this "directory of directories" would cast a very wide net, allowing much more than a narrow definition of what "directory" might allow.

This book takes an expanded notion of "directory," just as the Internet is expanding our notions of what information is, how it travels, and its value. There are many directories on the Internet. I have included these. There are directories, catalogs, and user guides about Internet. These, too, are included. There are also large numbers of lists—lists of mailing lists, lists of resources, lists of software depositories, and lists of directories. Since a directory is, after all, just a list, I was able to include many of these with good conscience. Another type of directory is found on file systems and FTP sites: a place where computer files are stored. A computer user might have hundreds of these directories in her possession. I have included pointers to some of the most important computer directories to be found on the Internet.

Acknowledgments

First thanks goes to my wife and partner, Ilana, for her help in collecting and verifying information and for just being there. Thanks to Tony Abbott and the editorial staff at Meckler for guidance and patience in creating the book. My colleagues and students at the Graduate School of Library and Information Science and the National Center for Supercomputing Applications at the University of Illinois spotted and forwarded to me many of the entries included in the book. This book was written on a Macintosh IIci on loan from Project Gutenberg, thanks to Michael S. Hart.

A work such as this can never truly be complete. Every day there are more resources being created on the Internet. If you create or are maintaining a resource, list, directory, user guide or other item, please keep the Internet community informed so that it may be included in a future edition.

Warranty

The author has made every effort to ensure that the information contained in this book is accurate at the time of printing. However, no warranty is offered as to the accuracy or completeness of the information in this book, and no responsibility is taken for any damages resulting from the use of its contents.

Trademarks

This book contains trademark and servicemark names. The publisher has indicated such names with an initial capital letter or by writing it as capitalized by the trademark or servicemark holder.

The listed copyright status for materials in this book does not supersede any claim to copyright or limitations on distribution that the author or publisher of a material may have made. In all cases the original source, author, or publisher should be consulted for full details on copyright status.

Formatting Notes

A. Fonts and Emphasis

I have tried to be consistent throughout this book in the formatting of commands and Internet addresses. Here is an overview of how things are presented:

Things you type, Internet nodes, and filenames are in Courier, for example: `ftp sunsite.unc.edu`

B. Data Format

A generic template was applied to each of the resources described in this book. Because of the diversity in the resources available, some variation in the field names and contents is present. Here is a brief description of the meaning and content of each component of the data format:

Title: Usually taken from the resource itself. Sometimes, when no specific title was available, a descriptive title was created.

Resource type: e.g., `List`, `Directory`, `Bibliography`, etc. (These are indexed at the back of the book).

Descriptive text: A brief description of the resource and its applicability.

Author: Who created the resource. Sometimes a `Corporate Author`. Other times, `Maintainer` or `Editor`.

Author affiliation/institution: Usually the same as the location where the resource may be found.

Author E-mail: Who to contact if additional information is needed about a resource.

Author postal address: Alternate contact method, if available.

Author telephone number: For most authors, E-mail is preferred to the telephone or postal contact.

File format: Description of file contents, from a computer's point of view. Usually either `text`, `source code`, or `program`.

Number of files: How many individual files make up the resource. For resources with more than one sub-theme this may be an approximation.

Data format: Description of file contents, from a human's point of view. Often `text`, sometimes `formatted text`, `list`, etc.

File size: Number of KB (kilobytes: thousands of bytes. 360KB could fit on a 5-1/4" double-sided double-density floppy disk), number of MB (megabytes: millions of bytes), and if appropriate the number of lines or pages when the file is printed or displayed.

Primary/authoritative source: Where to find it.

Instructions for access: How to get it.

Additional sources/methods: Other ways to retrieve it. Note that this is seldom exhaustive—many resources are held in multiple places and quite a few are accessible by tools such as WAIS or Gopher. The sources here are intended to be the most direct and are the first locations in which new versions are made available.

Last known revision date: From the document, the author, or the creation date of the file where the resource is stored.

Number of revisions to date: For some resources, such as lists and bibliographies, this is known. For multi-theme resources, such as FTP sites, the number of revisions is often unknown.

First issue: When the resource was first publicized or made widely available.

Next planned revision/planned frequency of revision: Obtained from the author, from the text, or extrapolated from the history of past revisions.

Copyright restriction: Any restriction on use of the resource. Please check with the resource's author before making assumptions about what you can and cannot do with a given resource. Generally, you are not permitted to sell or republish any materials without the consent of the author, regardless of whether a copyright restriction is contained in the text.

Experience level: Any special skills that might be needed to make use of the resource.

Target audience: Who the resource is specifically intended for.

Environment applicability: Some resources are limited in the computing environments in which they work. All resources assume network connectivity. This field is most often used to indicate resources that only work with a certain operating system, such as Unix or CMS.

Content sample: A sample entry or extract from the contents of many resources is provided.

Notes: Any additional information about the resources that is useful for employing it.

C. Shortened Reference Format

In places in which a full description of the methods for accessing a resource via anonymous FTP would be redundant or provide excessive detail, I have used the emerging short reference form for files on Internet that are accessible by Anonymous FTP. These citations have the general form of `host:/path/filename`, where:

- `host` is the Internet address of the site holding the file (use FTP to connect to it, provide `anonymous` as the username);

- `path` is the subdirectory. You will usually type `cd path`; and

- `filename` is the name of the file to retrieve. After typing `ascii` or `binary` (as needed for a plain text or binary format file), you will type `get filename`.

To retrieve the file referenced by `nic.ddn.mil:/rfc/rfc1432.txt` using most FTP software you would type this sequence of commands (responses from the remote system have been omitted, and I have used $ as my computer's prompt and FTP> as the FTP program's prompt):

```
$ ftp nic.ddn.mil
Username: anonymous
Password: gbnewby@uiuc.edu
FTP> cd rfc
FTP> ascii
FTP> get rfc1432.txt
```

1
Introduction

This Book is a Buffer Between You and a Severe Case of Information Overload

The Internet consisted of over 1,400,000 computers as of early 1993. That number will double within another year or so. Over 1,000 Internet computers (called nodes, hosts, or sites) stored data available for anonymous retrieval using a method called FTP. More than 2,000 public mailing lists, 300 libraries, and over 4,000 Usenet newsgroups were available—these are just the big categories.

Everyone has an interest, or a profession, or is part of some community. The Internet offers access to other people who have something in common with you. It also offers information resources to meet a tremendous variety of needs. Information is the substance of the Internet—information that is exchanged through formal or informal communication among individuals or groups and information that is broadcast or made accessible to the general Internet community.

The challenge of using the Internet effectively is not in finding information. The challenge is in finding information that you are interested in while avoiding the rest. We humans are well adapted to this sort of behavior, but most of us have not yet developed the skills in computer-mediated environments. We can focus in on a particular conversation at a party, we can identify the most important parts of a changing traffic pattern as we drive through it, and we can even "read" the Sunday newspaper without taking weeks to scan through every page and every advertisement. When searching across the Internet, though, most people have difficulty in avoiding distraction, and even the most expert Internet-ers get frustrated when things are not where they are expected to be.

Unlike a Sunday newspaper, few tangible components are encountered on the Internet. Unlike a traffic pattern, there are few signs—lights, large moving objects, sounds, and so forth—which help us to know where we are and what's going on. This is why it takes some time to develop sufficient network navigation skills to find what we want while not getting mired in the other stuff.

The lack of navigation cues is only one part of the problem of successful network use. Another part is that the items you are trying to use keep moving and changing—network addresses change, new services emerge, and more and more opportunities are created for you to get sidetracked.

Hence the *Directory of Directories on the Internet*. This is a book to help you to identify some of the "guideposts" on the Internet and the relations among different resources. It is aimed at all Internet users, old and new. For newer networkers, this book offers an overview of what's out there, and a way to focus in on some of the discussion forums and information services most likely to meet their needs. For a more experienced networker, this book is a reference tool for finding those resources that the user can remember seeing somewhere, but can't remember where.

The Internet is a shifting target. No single-volume book can list all of the resources available, and no such listing can stay current. This book does not attempt to identify resources themselves. Instead, it points to resources about resources: lists of lists, bibliographies, mailing lists, and resource guides that cover in detail a narrow domain. With this method, it is possible to maintain an overview of what's going on.

From the method of pointing to resources about resources also emerges a fundamental characteristic of the Internet: its bottom-up nature. The individual resources—mailing lists, information servers, and so forth—are maintained by individuals or small groups. Other individuals create guides to sets of resources for their own community (sometimes a geographic community, more often a networked community held together by common interests). It is on the work of this "cast of thousands" which this book is based.

The cast of thousands brings to mind another fundamental characteristic of the Internet: the power of individuals to have an effect. There is no "Internet resource creation committee" or any such entity. Instead, there are individuals and groups who have a desire to create something for themselves and, more often than not, to share their creation with the rest of the Internet community.

I invite and urge you to join the thousands. Take some steps toward making the Internet a more fruitful place to exchange messages to or find information. Remember that at the current rate of Internet growth, people who start using the Internet to their advantage in 1993 will be among the most experienced half of all users in 1994. All Internet users have the ability to improve the situation for those to come because the computer plus network puts us in a position to be an active creator, not just a recepient.

What This Book Does Not Do

This book does not attempt to teach you how to use the Internet. Instead I refer you to other books and your local computing support center. Although Chapter 2 presents the basics of the Internet navigation tools you will be using, it is not intended as a full tutorial for new users. The book is largely absent of examples, and most of those are generic—your Internet node might have very different software for accomplishing the same thing as someone else's, and you should have a basic familiarity with using it before going too far with the materials in this book.

The book is indexed extensively, and includes a summary of each resource. In all cases, the pointer to the resource location is the most authoritative one available. This can solve the problem of missing news about updates to resources because you do not use an authoritative source.

On Accessing the Resources in This Book

Many of the materials have an FTP host as the authoritative source. In Chapter 2, though, you will read about the important role that Gopher and some other tools are playing in making resources more accessible. In fact, a large proportion of the resources in this book may be found in Gopherspace. The problem is that Gopher menus change, and Gopherspace looks just a little different depending on the location of your entry point. This makes it very difficult to give unambigious Gopher directions. It is possible to give a Gopher document citation, in the same way I use FTP citations throughout this book. However, the Gopher citation is seldom, if ever, the authoritative one.

Resources come and go on the Internet. The resources in this book are relatively stable, and many may be found in more than one place. However, there is no guarantee that a given resource will stay where it is: information resource creators are sometimes at the mercy of system administrators who may choose to avoid providing materials to the rest of the Internet community.

Selection Criteria

This book contains items for which I was able to identify an authoritative source. When possible, I confirmed the data in the entries with the authors or resource providers. Some favorite resources needed to be left out of the book because I could not find an authoritative source, or because the author was no longer where he or she used to be, or because the resource was outdated. Generally, only materials that were updated in 1992 or after are included, although there are several exceptions.

The main criterion for inclusion is the same as is used in adding references to a term paper: only things that may be retrieved using their reference are included. Some items are created and widely disseminated but never archived effectively. Others are re-sent to mailing lists or newsgroups occasionally, but the original source or author is unknown. For the most part, I've left these out. Please do your part when redistributing network resources: include a full description of where the resource may be retrieved, and the name and e-mail address of the author if available.

A fair number of non-English items are included in this book, but not enough to represent the non-English components of the Internet. I have tried to include representative FTP sites and Gopher servers worldwide that may serve as access points to countries in which English is not the primary language.

A Moving Target

Not only do the resources and people behind them change, the growth of the Internet makes it very difficult to keep abreast of what resources are available in any particular area. The *Directory of Directories on the Internet* is here to help identify the resources of interest to you. It should serve as both a reference tool and a first stop when someone asks, "Hey, what's in the Internet for me?"

2
Tools for Networked Information Discovery and Retrieval

Tools That Are So Easy to Use That You Can Navigate the Network for Hours (and Still Not Necessarily Find What You Were Looking for)

This chapter will introduce the basics of the tools and methods for getting around the Internet. It will start with three building blocks: E-mail, telnet, and FTP. Then, four of the important tools for navigating the network will be described: Archie, Gopher, WAIS (Wide Area Information Servers), and WWW (the WorldWideWeb). These four tools are recent developments in networking that make interacting with networked resources much easier.

In the olden days of networking (say, before 1991), network navigators needed to be familiar with FTP and some telnet-accessible sites in order to find anything of value. They also needed to subscribe to several mailing lists to hear about new resources. Today, the tools described in this section make it far easier for all network users, especially new ones, to engage in network resource discovery and retrieval. Along with ease of use come two problems that recur in the descriptions of the tools. First is the relative lack of topic access. Second is the ability to get lost among interesting items that do not meet your specific need.

People who want to find something particular on the network—say a recipe for kumquat pie—may have difficulty in coming up with the right words to get to a place in which the recipe may be found. There probably are no filenames or Gopher menus with the word "kumquat" in them, and the word "recipe" might be found in too many. If our intrepid baker could get *inside* of the things he or she is searching, then the words "kumquat pie" might be useful. Instead, though, most tools necessitate taking educated guesses about where the object of desire is located, then going off and looking for it.

It used to be that network users could be generically placed in one of two categories. The first category included people who used the network for a purpose, such as reading a few E-mail lists and newsgroups. The second contained those who saw the network as its own purpose, who engaged in network navigation and resource discovery as an end unto itself. The tools described in this section make it far easier to be a member of the second category, and indeed necessitate a willingness to explore in order to find what's of relevance. With practice, you will be able to quickly identify a resource which is likely to contain an answer to your question. But it takes time to understand the various tools, and to build up a mental model of the types of resources which are most likely to contain what you are looking for.

4

This chapter is not intended as a user guide for these tools, although it will discuss their use in some detail. Your local system administrator or computing office should provide documentation on the specifics of using the tools in your environment.

E-mail

Electronic mail, also known as E-mail or email, is the lowest common denominator in computer networked communication. You can send E-mail to any user on any network, provided that there is a connection, or gateway, from your network to the network in which your target recipient is located.

An E-mail message is essentially a file with a special header. The header specifies from where the file is coming and to where it is going. In some cases, the E-mail might go directly from the sender to the recipient, such as when both users are on the same computer. In other cases, the message will get passed from computer to computer until it gets to the recipient's computer. Luckily, most network users do not need to worry too much about the path a message takes, because mail software and the network itself is "smart" about getting a message from one place to another.

Sometimes, you might need to get a message to another network. This involves the use of a gateway. In many cases, your E-mail software will know about the gateway and route your mail without you needing to tell it. However, at other times, you might need to specify the gateway explicitly. For example, someone on UUNet might have an address of this form:

```
host3!host2!host1!user
```

An Internet-based computer might not recognize the UUNet address. So to route the message from Internet (where you are) to UUNet (where you want the message to go), you need to send the message through a gateway, with an address of this form:

```
host3!host2!host1!user@uunet.uu.net
```

Because `uunet.uu.net` is an Internet node that is connected to both UUNet and Internet, it is able to gateway your message to the other network.

In accessing Internet resources, you will discover that there are a large number of E-mail addresses that are not associated with people. Instead, a computer program awaits incoming mail and processes it according to a set of rules. Such a program can be generically called a mail server. Mail servers might manage mailing lists, send you files on request, search a database, or even connect to other network resources. This book contains a large number of resources that are accessible via mail server. In practice, though, most of the resources are available more directly using some of the other tools mentioned in this chapter. Mail servers are most useful to people who are not on the same network as the resource. Because E-mail is the lowest common denominator, people who can not use telnet, FTP, Gopher, and so forth to get to the server (possibly because the server's network doesn't have those capabilities) can still get through using E-mail.

Telnet

Telnet is one of the services that distinguishes the Internet from other networks, such as BITNET and UUNet. Telnet is interactive access to remote computers via the Internet. When you use telnet to access a remote resource, your local computer system becomes transparent: you interact with the remote computer as though you were there, logged in directly. Because telnet is interactive, the network must be able to send messages between computers quickly enough so that the user doesn't notice that he or she is not using a local system. It must also be able to make a "direct" connection between any computer on the network.

Instead of having direct network connections between every pair of computers on the Internet (which would be quite expensive and inefficient), the Internet works a bit like the postal system: when you need to send a letter to someone, the post office does not use a special courier to route your message. Instead, it is routed with other messages that are going in the same general direction, and your message gets sorted out and rerouted as it goes. If you send two letters, they might not take the same path, but they will both get there. The Internet uses a concept called packet switching that is based on the post office metaphor to route "packets" of data between computers. Because each packet is small, and the network is fast, you can get messages through with minimal delay.

All computers on the Internet have a telnet command or a set of programs that do the same thing. Telnet requires a remote address to which to connect. This is variously called the IP address, the Internet address, the host or node name, and a few other things. You will recognize them by their hierarchical structure. Sometimes, they come in alphanumeric form, other times they are numeric only. Each Internet node has at least one IP address in numeric form, and most (but not all) have an alphanumeric equivalent.

Here's an example:

128.174.5.49   The IP address for a computer at the University of Illinois at Urbana-Champaign (UIUC).

ux1.cso.uiuc.edu   The alphanumeric equal. Both of these addresses will get you to the same machine!

A full description of Internet addressing schemes is beyond what you need to know to use the Internet effectively. Here are a few things you should know:

- *The alphanumeric version is usually safest to use.* This is because the physical machine associated with an alphanumeric address might change, as will the numeric IP address, but the services remain on the new machine with the same alphanumeric name.

- *Numeric IP addresses are more direct.* Alphanumeric addresses need to be looked up. It is possible that your local system can not find the right numeric address for the place you are trying to reach. That is a good time to try the numeric version.

- *Numeric and alphanumeric forms are reversed (except in the United Kingdom).* This means that in the address above the 128 part is associated with edu, the 174 with uiuc, the 5 with CSO, and the 49 is the number of the specific machine, ux1.

Telnet commands sometimes include a port number. Ports are used when the remote user wants to use a resource other than by logging on. By default, telnet will result in the remote machine asking for your username and password. By specifying a different port, you might instead be connected directly to a program that does not require a username/password. In fact, this is how E-mail is transferred on the Internet: by using a special port.

Here is an example of the use of a port in a telnet command (the command might not look exactly the same on your computer system):

```
telnet martini.eecs.umich.edu 3000
```

In that example, "3000" is the port number. If you try this, you will discover that a special geographic name service program will respond, and you will not be required to give a username or password. (For the detail hungry: there are some Internet nodes that do not require a username or password using the default telnet port. These are the exception, though, not the rule.)

FTP

FTP stands for File Transfer Protocol. This is a special method for transferring files between Internet nodes. Like E-mail, FTP is just telnet with a special port. Unlike E-mail, FTP requires a username and password to gain access to the remote system. One of the main uses of FTP is for people who need to transfer files between two different computers in which they have usernames. This could be used, for example, to create a dataset on one computer and analyze it on another.

The use for FTP that is of interest to Internet resource users is called "anonymous FTP." Anonymous FTP is FTP without the requirement that the FTP user be registered on the remote system. Usually, the user supplies "anonymous" as a username, and then supplies his or her E-mail address as a password (for the records of the anonymous FTP supplier).

Anyone who makes any sort of resource available by anonymous FTP—programs, data, publications, and so forth—only needs to publicize the Internet address of the machine in which the information is available. People can then use FTP to "log on" (in a limited sense) and transfer files. FTP is not the same as telnet in that the remote computer is not used transparently. Instead, you run a local program that interacts with the remote computer. Basically, FTP is good for finding out what files are available on the remote system (the equivalent of a ls, dir, or filelist command) and for copying files between the remote system and the local system. There are only a small number of commands available with FTP but they are sufficient for its purpose.

Most Internet nodes have an FTP command. Others might use different programs with the same functionality. On the Macintosh, the "Fetch" program is a nice point-and-click alternative to FTP syntax.

One of the difficulties in using FTP is knowing the type of file before it is transferred. Some systems need to know whether the file contains plain text or some sort of binary data (e.g., a program, or an image, or a compressed file). Another difficulty is that you might not know what is in a file until you retrieve it, if all you have to go by is a filename. A final difficulty is in knowing whether the file you retrieve will work for you. For example, if you use a computer running IBM's CMS operating system, you will not be able to do much with a Unix shell program. For plain text files, FTP is usually not a problem. For software, images, or binary data you need to know a bit more about what you are doing. Most of the resources in this book are plain text directories that point to other resources, so you do not need to worry too much about the details of FTP to copy and use these resources successfully.

Archie

Archie is a system for finding out about resources available via anonymous FTP. Because there are thousands of Internet nodes that store data available by anonymous FTP, which totals to terabytes (trillions of bytes) of data, it can be very difficult to find out which node to go to to retrieve a particular resource.

Once a month, Archie contacts all the FTP sites that it knows about and finds out what files are stored there (it rotates site contact times so that only a portion are contacted every night, with all sites being contacted by the end of the month). Archie maintains a database of all the files available at each place. Client software can search the database to find out where a particular file may be found.

Archie works very well, it solves many of the problems associated with finding Internet resources. If you know or can guess the filename that will be associated with what you are looking for, Archie can help you to find the nearest FTP site in which it may be retrieved. There is lots of redundancy in FTP sites—although no site carries everything, there is usually a benefit in transfer speed to be had from finding the node closest to you that has a particular file.

Archie does not get at the content of a file, so you still cannot do a keyword search on the topic you are looking for. It is also not exhaustive: many FTP sites are not found in Archie either because they are new, they moved, or Archie does not understand their FTP software or directory structure.

The Archie database is accessible in three ways. The first is by using a client program. This is a program that runs on your computer, solicits your query, and then interacts over the Internet with an Archie server to get the results. If you have an Archie client available, this will be most efficient. Second is via remote log on. There are currently twelve Internet nodes that allow remote log on for Archie searches. Finally, there is an Archie mail server for people without Internet access (in case you're wondering what they would do with the results: there is also FTP mail service for non-Internet users!).

Archie Servers

Archie Servers (may be queried with the Archie client, or may be logged onto with the username `archie`):

`archie.ans.net`	`archie.au`
`archie.doc.ic.ac.uk`	`archie.funet.fi`
`archie.Rutgers.edu`	`archie.sura.net`
`archie1.unl.edu`	`archie.cs.mcgill.ca`
`archie.sogang.ac.kr`	`archie.ncu.edu.tw`

The Archie mail server: Send a `help` message to `archie@ans.net` (other servers offer a mail option as well). Archie client and server software is available via anonymous FTP to `archie.cs.mcgill.ca`.

Gopher

Gopher has rapidly become a standard in Internet-based resource discovery and retrieval. It is also the basis for many recently created campus wide or corporate information systems. Gopher employs a simple hierarchical menu-oriented interface to enable users to navigate through network resources.

Unlike FTP and telnet, Gopher allows users to move transparently between different network nodes and directories. Thus, one Gopher can allow a user to move through the menu systems that lead to other Gopher sites. To the user, it appears as though all the resources are accessed from the same place, when in fact they might be anywhere on the Internet. In practice, different institutions maintain different collections of Gopher data, and organize them differently. In fact, though, a Gopher user can access almost any other Gopher server through his or her own local client.

Gopher uses a client-server method for interaction. Users run a client program (that usually runs on their local system—Gopher clients are available for all major operating systems), which interacts with a server. The server might be on the same machine as the client, or it can be anywhere across the Internet. In this book, I sometimes direct you to use a specific Gopher server. This might be accessible through your local Gopher servers (most if not all current Gopher servers offer access to other known Gopher servers), or you can connect to it directly.

If the "regular" Gopher command on your system is just to type:

```
gopher
```

you should be able to access the Gopher somewhere else, say at the University of Illinois at Urbana-Champaign, with a command of this form:

```
gopher gopher.uiuc.edu
```

Your software might have a different syntax, but still should be able to access different Gopher servers.

Gopher is a great blessing to those who have had difficulty in keeping all the different telnet and FTP sites straight. Gopher can also search databases using WAIS, and use telnet and FTP to access various remote resources. An associated tool, called "Veronica, " enables Gopher users to do keyword searches of "Gopherspace" in the same way that Archie allows users to search for terms in "FTP space."

Gopher makes network navigation much easier, but doesn't solve all problems. Although navigating through the Gopher menus might give hours of enjoyment, it is not well suited to finding specific resources or types of resources if you do not already know where to look (keyword searches using Veronica are still only on the brief Gopher menu text, which might not describe their content very well). Gopher might also leave a new user confused as they find themself in some telnet-accessible resource, or retrieving a binary file, or some other situation that at first seems inconsistent with the friendly text which makes up most of Gopherspace.

The ease with which Gopher servers may be started has resulted in a rapid increase in the number of corporations, campuses, and government institutions that provide network-accessible information. As Gopher matures, the client software will become easier to customize for a given user's purposes, and the seemingly haphazard organization of many Gopher sites will give way to better organized and more navigable schemes.

Wide Area Information Servers (WAIS)

WAIS is network-based information retrieval. Client programs query remote servers, give a query, and return with results. Because WAIS clients use the Internet to access remote databases, information seekers can very quickly find out whether several databases have any content of interest to them. Users do not need to log on to a remote server, and they do not need to know any query language for the particular database they are searching.

WAIS is based on a protocol called Z39.50. Z39.50 will soon be the basis of database sharing among commercially available library OPACs. WAIS clients have all the major operating systems available to them free of charge (but the system needs to be connected to Internet). WAIS servers may be built on most of these, making WAIS a viable solution to local data needs (e.g., to archive E-mail or to keep track of corporate communication).

WAIS is accessed by many Gopher sites (any menu option that ends with <?> is a WAIS database). WAIS databases currently number over 430. Most of these are not typical bibliographic databases for which you would use a CD-ROM or online retrieval system. Most Internet-accessible WAIS databases store data that were otherwise available on the Internet, but not as a searchable database. Archives of mailing lists and newsgroups, the index to RFCs and E-mail addresses, and so forth are typical—but there is lots of variety, including several full-text databases and a library catalog.

WAIS has brought information retrieval—the creation of query-able indexed databases—to the Internet. The clients are not all as simple to use as they should be, and the indexing and query types available are not yet as good as for most CD-ROM based information retrieval systems. However, the growth in numbers of WAIS databases and the ability for anyone to create an Internet-accessible database has enriched the access methods for networked information retrieval and discovery.

WordWideWeb (WWW)

The WorldWideWeb is Internet-based hypertext. WWW has the potential to solve one of the critical problems in network resource use: topic access. It also takes steps toward resolving difficulties in spotting relations among various resources or data items.

WWW suffers from the problem of other hypertext systems in that the links among data items (which may point anywhere to any resource on the network) must be inserted by hand. Given the terabytes of data and many hundreds of services currently accessible, this means that WWW is not a monolithic tool for accessing all the network resources (although links from WWW to Gopher and WAIS servers increases its scope). WWW is instead used to provide links among different resources, often in the form of links from *within* texts to other texts. WWW, like WAIS, gives users access beyond a simple filename or one-line menu entry.

WWW is not yet as widely used as WAIS and Gopher. Two telnet sites that offer WWW clients for remote log on as `info.cern.ch` and `eies2.njit.edu` (log on as www, lower case). WWW authoring software and a visual interface are under development at the National Center for Supercomputing Applications (NCSA), with prototype software for the X-Windows system available via anonymous FTP to `ftp.ncsa.uiuc.edu` (directory `pub/collage/xmosaic`).

As authoring tools and interfaces become easier to use, WWW will come into heavier use. The incorporation of hypertext links among data items make WWW much better suited for user documentation, help systems, resource information, and so forth than the other tools discussed in this system—provided someone takes the time to develop and test some intuitive links for users to follow.

Some Gopher Sites To Try

These may be connected to directly with a Gopher client. With most Gopher clients, you just need to type `gopher host` where `host` is the place you want to connect to. So, to get to the *UIUC Gopher,* you would type `gopher gopher.uiuc.edu`. In most cases you will need to explore the submenus to identify a particular resource.

If you do not have a local Gopher client, see if a nearby Internet site offers a public-access Gopher log on. Or, consult the list of public-access Gopher sites on page 20.

Note that ALL of these Gopher servers are available through the Gopher menu "Other Gopher and Information Servers" (or similar) found on most Gopher servers. If you are having trouble getting a menu that will get you to other Gopher servers on your home Gopher menu, try the first entry on the list on page 20. The rest of the list is in alphabetical order by the name of the institution that supports each server. When it is informative, a selected menu from the Gopher server is included with its description.

Gopher has rapidly become a standard tool for the dissemination of information at places which previously supported FTP sites, CWIS, or other services. Many other organizations are providing services for the first time because Gopher makes it easy.

Veronica is a keyword search tool that is available for all of Gopherspace. It does for Gopher what Archie does for FTP, except that it operates within Gopher and results in a new Gopher menu of all matches being displayed—so Veronica both finds a menu item and brings you to it.

`gopher.tc.umn.edu`   University of Minnesota

This is "Home of the Gopher." Gopher started at the University of Minnesota, at which there remains a clearinghouse for new Gopher servers and service upgrades. The associated FTP site is `boombox.micro.umn.edu`.

`fatty.law.cornell.edu`   Cornell Law School

A collection of legal information and information about law schools and their resources. There is also a WWW information service available.

1. About This Site (Cornell Law School).
2. Cornell Law School Information/
3. Directory of Legal Academia/
4. Discussions and Listserv Archives/
5. U.S. Law: Primary Documents and Commentary/
6. Foreign and International Law: Primary Documents and Commentary/
7. Other References Useful in Legal Education and Research/
8. Government Agencies: Information and Reports/
9. Information Services: Academic Institutions/
10. Library Resources (online catalogs)/
11. Periodicals, News, and Journals/

`ecosys.drdr.virginia.edu`   EcoGopher

An environmentally sound Gopher. This service focuses on U.S. ecological information, but also includes globally appropriate materials. The intent is to serve as a clearinghouse for all sorts of information about the environment and environmental activism.

1. Welcome to the EcoGopher Project!/
2. The University of Virginia Division of Recoverable and Disposable Resources.
3. The University of Virginia Environmental Programs/
4. Information: Environmental Organizations/
5. Action: Calendars, Campaigns, Programs, and Things To Do/
6. Communication: Electronic Mailing List Mailboxes/
7. Education: The EcoGopher Environmental Library/
8. Exploration: Gopher-accessible services/
9. Katie - Keyword-search of All Text In EcoGopher (coming soon!) <?>

`kaos.erin.gov.au`   The Environmental Resources Information Net-
                                      work [ERIN]

This is another environmentally sound Gopher. It contains information of special relevance to
Australia. People interested in Australia or environmentalism will find this server of interest.

1. ERIN Information - Systems Overview/
2. Biodiversity/
3. Protected Areas/
4. Terrestrial/ Marine Environments/
5. Environment Protection/
6. Legislation/
7. International Agreements/
8. Library Information/
9. General Information/

`laurel.euromath.dk`   Euromath

Euromath is a consortium of academic institutions in Europe devoted to the collection and
sharing of mathematical software and techniques among mathematicians. Materials are in
English and Danish.

`gopher.eu.net`   EUnet

EUnet is a European cooperative network offering a variety of services: "EUnet is the largest subscription-funded research-oriented network in Europe, serving users from Iceland to
Russia, and as far South as Tunisia. Operating since 1982, EUnet connects over four thousand sites and networks, with gateways to major research networks around the world including NSFnet and the Internet. One of the longest-operating R & D networks in Europe,
EUnet serves a large number of countries across a wide geographic area (from `EUnet
Overview`)." This Gopher server offers information about member countries, including
available network services in each country. It also provides links to the top-level Gopher
server in each member country, when available (in early 1993, the majority of countries had
relatively little information and no Gopher service).

`sunic.sunet.se`   European Root Gopher Server

This server is the gateway to (currently) over 130 Gopher servers in Europe and a variety of
other European information services.

Infoservers in European Countries

1. An_assembly_of_European_Gophers/
2. Austria/

3.   CONCISE (COSINE European Information Server) <TEL>
4.   Denmark/
5.   Descriptions of European Networks/
6.   ECHO (through SWITCH) <TEL>
7.   EUROKOM <TEL>
8.   EUnet entry point/
9.   European National Entrypoints/
10. Finland/
11. France/
12. Germany/
13. Greece/
14. Iceland/
15. Italy/
16. Netherlands/
17. Norway/
18. Poland/
19. Portugal/
20. RIPE NCC (Information Server for the European IP-Network)/
21. Slovakia/
22. Spain/
23. Sweden/
24. Switzerland/
25. United Kingdom/

`gopher.georgetown.edu`   Georgetown University

This is the location of the Catalogue of Projects in Electronic Text (CPET), which creates digests of new resources for electronic texts. The digests include descriptive information about how to access the texts.

"Now digests of project information—organized by humanities discipline and by language of the electronic text—can be read, searched, and retrieved by means of the Internet's protocols for Gopher and anonymous FTP. There are digests for 40 different languages, as well as for linguistics, literature, philosophy, biblical studies, and a variety of others, ranging from Medieval and Renaissance studies to Archaeology, African studies, and Buddhism." (From an announcement by the project assistant, Paul Mangiafico <pmangiafico@guvax.georgetown.edu>.) Also available via FTP to ftp.georgetown.edu.

`mentor.lanl.gov`   LANL Physics Information Service

Materials about physics, including electronic journals, abstracts, and pointers to various resources.

1.   Welcome - LANL Physics Information Service - CHANGES (updated Marc...
2.   Links to Similar Servers/
3.   —— Preprint Lists ——.

   4.   Abstracts of Recent Papers (gr-qc, hep-lat, hep-ph, hep-th, and nu../

   5.   Algebraic Geometry/

   6.   Astrophysics/

   7.   Condensed Matter Physics/

   8.   Functional Analysis/

   9.   General Relativity & Quantum Cosmology/

10.   High Energy Physics - Lattice/

11.   High Energy Physics - Phenomenology/

12.   High Energy Physics - Theory/

13.   Nuclear Theory/

14.   ———- Eprint Related Information ———-.

15.   Eprint Related Software/

16.   Index to gr-qc, hep-lat, hep-ph, hep-th, and nucl-th abstracts <?>

17.   ———- Other Information ———-.

18.   Physics News (Newsletters, Conferences, etc.)/

`gopher.lysator.liu.se`   Linkoping University, Linkoping, Sweden

A nice Gopher server. Menus are offered in "wide" or "deep" form, either English or Swedish, for the same information. The collection includes an archive of Science Fiction reviews and information, and Project Runeberg, a collection of public-domain Swedish etexts.

   1.   H E L P   !......This menu has far too many lines/

   2.   ...Jag vill hellre se svenska menyer/

   3. —> —>   Scandinavian Texts On-line/

   4. —> —>   Science Fiction Archive/

   5.   Newcomers.......Welcome to Lysator's Gopher Service.

   6.   ..This is Lysator, Linkoping, Sweden.

   7.   ...Meet friends (KOM, irc, mail, ...)/

   8.   ...Play games (MUD, Go, Galactic bloodshed, ...)/

   9.   ...Search and find information (gopher, ftp, ...)/

10.   Societies....Admittansen (electronics) (in Swedish).

11.   ...Ctrl-C (computers) (in Swedish).

12.   ...LiTHsa SK5EU (ham radio).

13.   ..Lysator (computers) (in Swedish)/

14.   ...Other university computer clubs/

15.   Projects.   ....Project Runeberg, Scandinavian e-texts/

16.   ...Electronic text projects elsewhere/

17.   ...RydNET, networking student homes/

18.   ...USENET University/

19.   Tourism   ...Local museums and interesting places/

20.   People.   .....Names, addresses, birthdays, photos/

21. Politics ...Programming freedom and free programs/
22. Technical..National statistics, facts, figures/
23. ...LINUX (the PC UNIX)/
24. ...Other operating systems/
25. ...Data communications, networking/
26. ...Programming languages/
27. Gopher ...Administration of Gopher servers/
28. ...Nordic and Swedish servers/
29. ...Servers in Europe/
30. ...Servers in the rest of the world/
31. ...Utrikiska Gopher-databaser/
32. .Vvriga obskyra underrubriker/

`gopher.ncc.edu.jp`   National Cancer Center (Japan)

This Gopher contains two types of information. First is cancer data, which partially mirrors `nih.edu` (below). Second is a collection of items about life in Japan.

Japan Information

1. 00README.
2. Events/
3. Food/
4. Geography/
5. History/
6. University information/

`nih.edu`   The National Institute of Health (U.S.)

This Gopher server includes CancerNet, a cancer information system with current information and guidelines, intended primarily for doctors.

NIH Information

1. NIH Office of Education/
2. NIH Guide to Grants and Contracts/
3. CancerNet Information/
4. NIH Calendar of Events—This Week— (Yellow Sheet).
5. NIH Calendar of Events—Next Week—(Yellow Sheet).

`stis.nsf.gov`   National Science Foundation Gopher

The National Science Foundation (U.S.) maintains a collection of project abstracts, funding bulletins, and Requests for Proposals that is an important stop for those interested in NSF funding. The abstracts of funded projects constitute a very current source of who is doing what in NSF-funded science.

1.   About this Gopher.
2.   About STIS/
3.   Index to NSF Award Abstracts <?>
4.   Index to NSF Publications <?>
5.   NSF Publications/
6.   BIO - Dir. for Biological Sciences/
7.   CISE - Dir. for Computer and Information Science and Engineering/
8.   EHR - Dir. for Education and Human Resources/
9.   ENG - Dir. for Engineering/
10.   GEO - Dir. for Geosciences/
11.   MPS - Dir. for Math and Physical Sciences/
12.   NSB - National Science Board/
13.   OIG - Office of the Inspector General/
14.   Office of the Director/
15.   SBE - Dir. for Social, Behavioral and Economic Sciences/
16.   SRS - Science Resources Studies Division/

`solomon.technet.sg`   TECHNET, Singapore's Island-wide Network

Travel and general information about Singapore. This Gopher currently links to three other Singapore Gopher servers.

Singapore — Island, City, State

1.   Welcome To Singapore.
2.   SIFlash — Singapore International Foundation's Newsletter/
3.   HitchHiker — Technet's Quarterly Newsletter/

`blaze.trentu.ca`   Trent University

A well-organized Gopher with an excellent collection of "resource guides." Unlike the content of the Resource Guides chapter in this book, the guides accessible here are shorter and directed at a narrow audience. Many of the resources in this menu are no longer current, or are otherwise difficult to retrieve. A very good place to browse.

Internet Resource Guides

1.   About these Guides....
2.   Academic Discussion Lists and Interest Groups/
3.   Alt.internet.services FAQ.
4.   Anonymous FTP/
5.   Biologist's Guide to Internet Resources.

6. Business Resources on the Internet.
7. Electric Mystic's Guide to the Internet.
8. Electronic Sources for Western European History and Culture.
9. Hitchhikers Guide to the Internet.
10. How to find E-mail addresses.
11. Internet Resources for Earth Sciences/
12. Library Resources on the Internet/
13. Library-Oriented Computer Conferences and E-Serials.
14. Network Knowledge for the Neophyte.
15. Online Health Resources List.
16. Other Internet Documents/
17. Search the list of mailing lists <?>
18. Short Bibliography of Introductory Internetworking Readings.
19. Social Scientists Guidebook: A Guide to the Internet.
20. Sources of Meteorological Data FAQ.
21. Sources: The Internet and Computer-Mediated Communication.
22. Special Internet Connections.
23. There's Gold in Them Thar Networks!
24. Using Networked Information Resources
25. Venturing Into the Internet.
26. Where To Start - A Bibliography of Internetworking Information.
27. Zen and the Art of the Internet.

`gopher.uiuc.edu`   University of Illinois at Urbana-Champaign

Among other things, this is the source of the UIUC Weather Server, a central resource for up-to-the-minute weather forecasts. Satellite images are also available (stored in "gif" format).

`gopher.unt.edu`   University of North Texas

Maintains one of the net's most comprehensive collections of electronic journals.

Newsletters and Journals

1. Art/
2. Bryn Mawr Classical Review <?>
3. CICNET collection/
4. Campus newspapers/
5. Computing/
6. Education/
7. Humanities/
8. International Academy of Hospitality Research/
9. Journal of Tech. Edu./

10. Languages/
11. Law and Politics Book Review/
12. Library/
13. Medical/
14. News From Earth/
15. Political Newsletters/
16. Religious\Cultural/
17. Science/
18. UNT NetMan/

`gopher.up.ac.za`   University of Pretoria

During the Tiananmen Square incident in China, the breakup of the Soviet Union, and the war in Iraq, the world network community received news updates from people in the affected areas, even when the regular media was denied access. Until recently, there has been almost no network traffic between South Africa and the rest of the Internet. It seems that the winds of change may now blow via computer network.

University of Pretoria, South Africa

1. Welcome to the University of Pretoria Gopher.
2. University of Pretoria/
3. Information About Gopher/
4. Internet Libraries/
5. Internet file server (ftp) sites/
6. Other Gopher Servers/
7. Other Gopher Servers in South Africa/
8. Other Information Sources/
9. Phonebooks/
10. Public Information Networks/
11. Special Internet Services (from Scott Yanoff)/
12. The Internet Hunt/
13. WorldWideWeb <TEL>

`bigcheese.math.scarolina.edu`   University of South Carolina

One of the richest Gopher servers, with a great diversity of Internet resources that can be accessed from a concise menu tree. The signal-to-noise ratio is very favorable here.

Distributed Multi-Topic Info[sic] Resources

1. * Coombs Papers/
2. * Electronic Books - Gutenberg collection (UMN)/
3. * Newspapers, Magazines, and Newsletters (UMN)/
4. * Online Book Initiative (world.std.com)/

5. * Research and Technical Reports/
6. > Major Collections at other servers/
7. > Misc. Collections at other servers/
8. Computer Information/
9. Education/
10. Incoming/
11. Library of Congress archives/
12. Minority/
13. Miscellaneous/
14. Music/
15. Presidential Campaign '92 Documents/
16. Reference Works (UMN)/
17. Religion/
18. Science and Technology/
19. Social Science/
20. Statistics/
21. Weather Information/

`wiretap.spies.com`   Spies in the Wire (WIRETAP)

This Gopher site contains a wide-ranging collection of speeches, press releases, executive orders, and so forth relating to the Clinton Administration. All texts are also available via anonymous FTP to `wiretap.spies.com`.

From The top level README file:

Clinton	White House Press Releases
Economic_Plan	Clinton's Economic Plan
GAO_Reports	GAO Transition Reports
NAFTA	North American Free Trade Agreement
alt.etext	Usenet alt.etext Archives

Public-Access Gopher Sites

These Internet sites offer free anonymous log ons for use of Gopher services. They should be used only by those who do not have their own Gopher server. Note that Gopher servers are available for all major computer types.

Taken from `pit-manager.mit.edu:/pub/usenet/Gopher_` `(comp.infosystems.gopher)_Frequently_Asked_Questions_(FAQ)`.

Hostname	IP#	Log on	Area
consultant.micro.umn.edu	134.84.132.4	gopher	North America
gopher.uiuc.edu	128.174.33.160	gopher	North America

panda.uiowa.edu	128.255.40.201	panda	North America
gopher.sunet.se	192.36.125.2	gopher	Europe
info.anu.edu.au	150.203.84.20	info	Australia
gopher.chalmers.se	129.16.221.40	gopher	Sweden
tolten.puc.cl	146.155.1.16	gopher	South America
ecnet.ec	157.100.45.2	gopher	Ecuador
gan.ncc.go.jp	160.190.10.1	gopher	Japan

Title: WAIS Software
Resource Type: Software

WAIS software is available free of charge for most major computing platforms. To use networked WAIS sources, your computer must be connected to the Internet. However, you can also use WAIS software to create a searchable database on your own computer. WAIS has seen some very recent changes that indicate the CNIDR FTP host for WAIS will become the authoritative one, instead of the Thinking Machines host.

Authors: Thinking Machines, Inc. (primary); Coalition for Networked Information Discovery and Retrieval (CNIDR) (primary); Office of Information Technology, University of North Carolina at Chapel Hill (additional); United States Geological Survey (USGS) (additional)

Author USPS address: WAIS Inc., 1040 Noel Drive, Menlo Park, CA 94025
Author E-mail: Info@wais.com
Author telephone number: (415) 327-WAIS
File name: Various, according to platform
File formats: Source code and executable files
File size: Varies according to platform. From about 500KB to 1.5MB

Primary/authoritative sources: `ftp think.com` and `ftp ftp.oit.unc.edu` and `ftp ftp.cnidr.org` (these sites do not have identical holdings)
Instructions for access: `cd wais` (on `think.com`) or `cd pub/wais` (on `ftp.oit.unc.edu`) or `cd pub/wais/freeWAIS` (on `ftp.cnidr.org`). Use `dir` and `cd` to identify the software you want.

Last known revision date: March 1993
Number of revisions to date: New platforms have been added every few months by the UNC programmers. Currently, all major hardware platforms are supported to some extent except IBM mainframes.
First issue: Spring 1991
Next planned revision/planned frequency of revision: Software is updated periodically on no particular schedule.

Copyright restriction: WAIS software may be used, modified, or distributed freely. Commercial use is permitted.

Experience level: System administration skills and system privileges are needed to install most versions of WAIS server software. However, the Windows and Macintosh Hypercard versions of the client software are very easy to install, even for relative novices.

Target audience: Multiple databases are available to meet the needs of many audiences. Additionally, server software allows one to create his or her own databases easily.

Environment applicability: WAIS client software currently exists only for computers that are connected to the Internet. The software runs on Macintosh, IBM-compatible (with Windows), Unix (under various windowing systems), and NeXT computers. A simple WAIS interface for Unix based on the vt100 terminal is also available, but is not recommended for new users.

Note: E-mail mailing lists exist for discussion of WAIS. Send a command to `list-serv@think.com` for one of the two available mailing lists. `wais-discussion` is for biweekly updates, `wais-talk` is a developers discussion list. Note that these lists are not maintained by the standard CMS LISTSERV software and that the syntax is somewhat different:

```
subscribe <full-email-address> wais-discussion
```

or

```
subscribe <full-email-address> wais-talk
```

Anonymous log ons exist for the vt100 client interface. This interface is not nearly as powerful as the window-based interfaces. To access the vt100 interface, `telnet quake.think.com` and log on as `wais`.

The CNIDR version of freeWAIS may be the only one to be frequently updated for the future.

Title: WAIS Directory of Servers
Resource Type: List

This is a WAIS source that may be used to search for other WAIS sources. Because the number of sources grows weekly, this is a good place to start a WAIS search.

Authors: Multiple. Contact information is listed within the source description file, which is retrievable via WAIS.

File name: Directory-of-servers.src
File formats: WAIS source file
Data format: Formatted text
File size: Thirty-two lines

Content details: This WAIS source contains the information needed to access any known WAIS source. There are over 430 WAIS sources, containing data of widely varying types. Full text, bibliographic data, images, and sound may all be accessed by WAIS, provided your WAIS client knows of an application to display the data.

Primary/authoritative source: `ftp quake.think.com`
Instructions for access: `cd wais; get wais-servers.tar.Z.` uncompress and detar `wais-sources/directory-of-servers.src`

Additional sources/methods:

1. `ftp.oit.unc.edu` keeps the same file.
2. WAIS client and server software always comes with this one source
3. A Macintosh version of all WAIS sources is available from `ftp.oit.unc.edu`.

Last known revision date: March 1993
Number of revisions to date: Hundreds
First issue: Spring 1991

Next planned revision/planned frequency of revision: Updated as new sources are publicized. Occasionally sources may be deleted.

Copyright restriction: WAIS software and all sources may currently be freely distributed. Commercial use is permitted. Generally, only individual records from the data are retrievable, not the actual source data.

Experience level: Moderate experience with WAIS is needed to effectively select new sources. Depending on the platform chosen, a high level of experience may be needed to install the WAIS software itself.

Target audience: Depends on the source.

Environment applicability: Any WAIS client may search this database. Current WAIS software is limited to computers which are connected to Internet. The software runs on Macintosh, IBM-compatible (with Windows), Unix (under various windowing systems), and NeXT computers. A simple WAIS interface based on the vt100 terminal is also available, but is not recommended for new users.

Notes: A charging mechanism is built into WAIS, so it is likely that some sort of cost will be involved in some database use in the future.

3
Resource Guides

Why a Monolithic Guide Might Be Your Best First Stop

"Resource guide" is a term applied to texts that point to various networked resources. Many guides strive to serve a particular user group or region. The chances are good that your local institution produces some documents that might be called "resource guides."

This chapter lists some of the best resource guides available via the Internet (and one or two that are not network-accessible but are still worth looking at). There are several advantages to using resource guides to identify network resources:

- Resource guides are usually formatted for printing, to be kept as a hard-copy reference.

- Resource guides contain more complete information about a resource than might be immediately available online.

- Resource guides are arranged topically.

- Resource guides include selected resources, which helps to narrow the universe of Internet-accessible items to those in which you are most interested.

In short, resource guides can make up for some of the difficulties in using Internet-based resources by providing "meta-information," or information about the resources.

These guides are not a panacea, of course. They are generally not up to date with the newest resources, and all the guides listed here provide enough information about each resource that they cannot serve easily as a "quick reference." Resource guides usually do not provide a great amount of detail and may have little direct pertinence to a particular user or user group. The next stop a new user might make after consulting a resource guide is a mailing list or newsgroup where like-minded people are discussing items of interest. Chapter 8 of this book contains a listing of such discussion forums.

New network users, or network information centers, should choose one or two resource guides for their general use. Because it is well-maintained and has a large scope, *The Internet Resource Guide* should almost definitely be one of the guides chosen. I hope that the new home of the *IRG* will continue to produce similar high-quality resources.

Title: AARNet Resource Guide
Resource Type: Resource Guide

This is the guide of the Australian Academic Research Network (AARNet). It contains general network information, as well as quite a bit relevant mostly to Australian residents. The guide does not provide general information on how to use the Internet or specific resources. Instead, it acts as a directory of contact information for the individual resources.

Author: AARNet
Author E-mail: AARNet@aarnet.edu.au
Author telephone number: +06-249-3385

File format: Text or compressed text
Number of files: Six of each type
Data format: Text or PostScript
File size: Text files total 234KB, 11,358 lines

Primary/authoritative source: `ftp jatz.aarnet.edu.au`
Instructions for access: `cd pub/resource-guide; mget` either `*.txt` or `*.ps` or `*.ps.Z`
Additional sources/methods: None

Last known revision date: January 1993
Number of revisions to date: Unknown
First issue: Unknown
Next planned revision/planned frequency of revision: Unknown

Copyright restriction: None

Experience level: General
Target audience: General, but with a focus on the Australian and New Zealand communities.

Content summary (from pub/resource-guide/README):

aarnet_resource_guide.frm	Form to fill-in to submit a resource guide entry
resource_guide_netmembers.*	AARNet member descriptions
resource_guide_compresources.*	Computational resources on AARNet
resource_guide_libraries.*	Library OPAC accessible over AARNet
resource_guide_directories.*	Directory Services on AARNet
resource_guide_netgateways.*	Network Gateways on AARNet

Content sample (from resource_guide_compresources.txt):

The Australian National University Supercomputer Facility

Address:
    ANUSF
    Computer Services Centre
    Australian National University
    GPO Box 4
    Canberra 2601

E-mail: anusf@anusf.anu.edu.au
Phone: +616 249 3437
Fax: +616 249 3425

Description: The ANUSF operates a Fujitsu VP-100 supercomputer. The VP-100 is rated at 285Mflops peak speed, has a sophisticated vectorising Fortran compiler, and optimization tools.

Title: An Incomplete Guide to the Internet
Resource Type: Resource Guide

This resource guide is subtitled "and Other Telecommunications Opportunities Especially for Teachers and Students K-12." It includes descriptions of the basic Internet tools—email, telnet, FTP—and then discusses some resources of pertinence to people in K-12 environments, such as FrEdMail. Netiquette is covered, and several project ideas for K-12 students and teachers are introduced.

Authors: Brian Golden and Charles Farmer
Additional contact: Lisa Bievenue
Author affiliation/institution: National Center for Supercomputing Applications (NCSA)
Author E-mail: bievenue@ncsa.uiuc.edu
Author postal address: Computing Applications Building, University of Illinois at Urbana-Champaign, Urbana, IL 61801
Author telephone number: (217) 244-1993

File format: Text
Number of files: One
Data format: Rich Text Format (rtf) suitable for import to a word processor
File size: 2.4MB; about 275 pages when printed

Primary/authoritative source: `ftp ftp.ncsa.uiuc.edu`
Instructions for access: `cd Education; get IncompleteGuide.rtf`
Additional sources/methods: The guide is also available free of charge in print form. Contact Lisa Bievenue at the address above.

Last revision: January 1993
Number of revisions to date: 1
First issue: Fall 1992
Next planned revision/planned frequency of revision: Unknown

Copyright restriction: None

Experience level: Introductory
Target audience: K-12 educators

Table of Contents:

Title: BITNET Servers
Resource Type: Resource Guide

This is a very nice guide to BITNET resources. Although many items that are available via BITNET are accessible to Internet users via FTP or other means, there are still a number of items that are of value to BITNET users that are not directly accessible via Internet. This list contains items of both types, including electronic journals, file servers, a listing of sites running LISTSERV software, sites with user directory services, and lists of RELAY sites (RELAY is a BITNET version of the popular Internet Relay Chat or IRC which Internet users employ to have multi-user networked conversations).

Author: Christopher Condon
Author affiliation/institution: Yale University
Author E-mail: bitlib@yalevm.ycc.yale.edu

File format: Text
Number of files: One
Data format: Formatted list
File size: 1,300 lines

Primary/authoritative source: `netserv@bitnic.educom.edu`
Instructions for access: Send E-mail message `send bitnet servers`
Additional sources/methods: Other netserv machines also store this file.

Last known revision date: July 1991
Number of revisions to date: Unknown
First issue: Unknown
Next planned revision/planned frequency of revision: None anticipated

Copyright restriction: None

Target audience: BITNET users
Environment applicability: Applies mostly to BITNET users, but Internet users will be able to access some of the services.

Content sample:

BITFTP @ PUCC - Princeton University

FTP (or File Transfer Protocol) is the Internet method of transferring non-mail files (be they text, formatted data, or programs). People on the Internet can "login" to an FTP server at a remote site and download files. The process is in many ways similar to dialing up a bulletin board with a PC, although it is thankfully much faster. BITNET users can now access these FTP servers through BITFTP. To use BITFTP, send mail containing your FTP commands to "BITFTP@PUCC". The first command BITFTP must be "FTP" or "HELP". Accepts commands via MAIL.

Note: Although this list is dated, a good proportion of the servers it lists are still active.

Title: CICNet Resource Guide
Resource Type: Resource Guide

The level of description and completeness of the information in this guide is especially good. The guide includes information of direct relevance to the CICNet service area (midwestern United States), but most is applicable to a general audience.

Editor: John Holbrook
Editor affiliation/institution: CICNet
Institution email: info@cic.net
Institution postal address: 2901 Hubbard Road, Ann Arbor, MI 48109
Institution telephone number: (313) 998-6103

File format: Text
Number of files: One
Data format: Text or PostScript
File size: 381KB; 9194 lines (text version)

Primary/authoritative source: `ftp ftp.cic.net`
Instructions for access: `cd pub/resourceguide; ascii; get cicnetguide-1.0a.txt`. PostScript and compressed versions are also available.
Additional sources/methods: The contents are also available via Gopher to `gopher.cic.net`, where they are searchable as a WAIS source (the WAIS source may be searched from elsewhere as well. The .src file is in the same directory as the resource guide).

Last known revision date: June 1992
Number of revisions to date: 0
Next planned revision/planned frequency of revision: 1993

Copyright restriction: "Parts of this document Copyright (c) 1991 by NYSERNet, Syracuse, New York. All rights reserved. No part of this document may be reproduced in any form or by any means, without permission from CICNet, Inc. or NYSERNet."
Experience level: General
Target audience: General, with some focus on CICNet resources

Table of contents:

1. CICNet Resources
2. Internet Navigation Tools
3. Guides and Directories
4. Research/Supercomputer Resources
5. Libraries
6. Library Applications and Related Resource
7. Campus Wide Information Systems
8. Internet Resources

Content sample (partial entry):

5.4. OCLC: World's Largest Bibliographic Database
Last verified: April 92

Access to more than twenty-two million books and other library materials on the OCLC union catalog as well as other commercial and noncommercial databases.

Availability: Authorization and password are required to use the service.

Access: telnet epic.prod.oclc.org

Note: Printed and bound hard copies of *The CICNet Resource Guide* may be obtained from CICNet. Price: $15 for CICNet members, $27 for nonmembers

Title: Internet Resource Guide
Resource Type: Resource Guide

This was one of the first widely distributed general resource guides and remains an excellent first stop for seeking out Internet-based resources. Most of the resources included in the IRG are for academics, professionals, or scholars, but with a very multidisciplinary scope.

The IRG has been recently moved to a new "home," and will no longer be maintained as before. Instead, the InterNIC Information Service (see page 126) will incorporate and expand the listings contained in the Internet Resource Guide.

Author: National Science Foundation Network Service Center
Author affiliation/institution: National Science Foundation (U.S.)

Author E-mail: nnsc@nnsc.nsf.net
Current maintainer: AT&T
Current maintainer E-mail: admin@ds.internic.net
Current maintainer postal address: 5000 Hadley Road, Room 1B13, South Plainfield, NJ 07080
Current maintainer telephone: (908) 668-6587

File format: Text, compressed text, or tar file
Number of files: Depends on format
Data format: Text or PostScript
File size: Depends on format, from several KB to over 500KB

Primary source: `ftp nnsc.nsf.net`
Instructions for access: `cd resource-guide`; `ls`, `cd`, and `get` to identify and retrieve files
Additional sources/methods: Copies of the IRG are available from several anonymous FTP sites.

Last known revision date: March 1993
Number of revisions to date: Unknown
First issue: Unknown
Next planned revision/planned frequency of revision: None

Copyright restriction: Copyright 1989-1992 BBN Systems and Technologies (see the IRG for details).

Experience level: Some Internet experience is desirable.
Target audience: General, but many resources listed are aimed at a particular audience.

Table of Contents:

    Chapter 1:   Computational Resources
    Chapter 2:   Library Catalogs
    Chapter 3:   Archives
    Chapter 4:   White Pages
    Chapter 5:   Networks
    Chapter 6:   Network Information Centers
    Chapter M: Miscellaneous

Title: *NorthWestNet User Services Internet Resource Guide*
Resource Type: *Resource guide*

This is a well-done resource guide that breaks the resources into different categories, including categories for particular user groups. However, it has not been updated since it was first issued.

Corporate Author: NorthWestNet
Author E-mail: nusirg-orders@nwnet.net
Author postal address: 15400 SE 30th Place, Suite 202, Bellevue, WA 98007
Author telephone number: (206) 562-3000
File format: PostScript
Number of files: One
Data format: Text (when printed with a PostScript printer)
File size: Over 1.4MB for the entire document, 300 pages

Primary/authoritative source: `ftp ftphost.nwnet.net`
Instructions for access: `cd nic/nwnet/user-guide; get README.nusirg` for
information about getting the whole guide
Additional sources/methods: None

Last known revision date: 1991
Number of revisions to date: Unknown
First issue: 1991
Next planned revision/planned frequency of revision: Unknown

Copyright restriction: None

Experience level: General
Target audience: General, but with a focus on NorthWestNet regional services

Content note: (from `README.nusirg`) The online version of NUSIRG is available only
in PostScript format. The document is available in parts or in its entirety, and the following
files are available from this directory:

Filenames	*Brief Description of Contents*
README.nusirg	(this file
nusirg.Index.ps	(Index for all of NUSIRG
nusirg.about.nwnet.and.aup.ps	(Info about NWNET and NSFNET
nusirg.beginner.overview.ps	(Overview of NUSIRG and the Internet
nusirg.email.ftp.telnet.ps	(E-mail, FTP, TELNET and Archie
nusirg.listserv.usenet.ps	(USENET and LISTSERV
nusirg.online.info.resources.ps	(Electronic books, electronic
	(journals, online library catalogs,
	(databases and bibliographies,
	(WAIS, and Internet directories
nusirg.supercomputers.ps	(Supercomputers on the Internet
nusirg.teach.k-12.ps	(The Internet and K-12 education
nusirg.whole-guide.ps.Z	(All of NUSIRG in compressed
	(format

Note: The guide is available bound on paper for $20 from NorthWestNet, NUSIRG Orders, 15400 SE 30th Place, Suite 202, Bellevue, WA 98007.

Title: New User's Guide to Useful and Unique Resources on the Internet
Resource Type: Resource Guide

This resource guide was produced by NYSERNet, the regional network of New York State. It includes a nice collection of resources, but a somewhat smaller collection than some other resource guides. This is an advantage for new users, though, and the resources included are appropriately chosen to meet NYSERNet's diverse population of users.

Corporate author: NYSERNet, Inc.
Author E-mail: editor@nysernet.org
Author postal address: 111 College Place, Syracuse, NY 13244-4100
Author telephone number: (315) 443-4120

File format: Text
Number of files: One
Data format: Text
File size: 307KB, 8,207 lines

Primary/authoritative source: `ftp nysernet.org`
Instructions for access: `cd pub/resources/guides; ascii; get`
`new.user.guide.v2.2.txt`
Additional sources/methods: None (but see Note below)

Last known revision date: April 1992
Number of revisions to date: two major, several minor
First issue: 1991
Next planned revision/planned frequency of revision: Unknown

Copyright restriction: Copyright 1992, NYSERNet, Syracuse, New York

Experience level: General, nonspecialist
Target audience: New users, but suitable as a reference guide to general Internet resources for more experienced users
Environment applicability: All resources are physically based in the U.S.

Content sample:

ClariNet: The Electronic Newspaper

Service: Full-text newsfeed including wireservice as well as professional and industry news. Data is transmitted to subscribers and can then be read, manipulated, and filtered using USENET software such as "rn" (readnews).

ClariNet Communications Corp. 124 King St. N., Waterloo, Ontario, N2J 2X8   800/USE-NETS

Brief Table of Contents:

1. Library Catalogs & Campus Information Systems
2. Databases
3. Electronic Discussion Groups/Forums
4. Directories
5. Information Resources
6. FTP Archives
7. Fee-Based Information Services
8. Software/Freeware
9. Bulletin Board Services
10. Miscellaneous

Note: Paper copies are available for $25 U.S. ($18 for NYSERNet affiliates). Contact the authors.

Title: SURAnet Guide to Selected Internet Resources
Resource Type: Resource Guide

This guide offers a general introduction to Internet and full descriptions of some specific resources. Good instructions are provided for the new network user. The Guide has less information of a strictly regional flavor than other mid-level network guides.

Corporate Author: SURAnet Network Information Center
Author E-mail: info@sura.net
Author postal address: 8400 Baltimore Blvd., College Park, MD 20740-2498
Author telephone number: (301) 982-4600

File format: Text
Number of files: One
Data format: Text
File size: 143KB, 4,395 lines

Primary/authoritative source: `ftp ftp.sura.net`
Instructions for access: `cd pub/nic; ascii; get infoguide.3-93.txt` (the 3-93 will change to other dates as new versions are released)
Additional sources/methods: None

Last known revision date: March 1993
Number of revisions to date: Unknown
First issue: 1992
Next planned revision/planned frequency of revision: Unknown

Copyright restriction: None

Target audience: General, but with a focus on the novice user

Table of Contents:

Title: Surfing the Internet
Resource Type: Resource Guide

This is a relatively short but quite useful introduction to the capabilities of the Internet and a listing of some general resources. The focus in on guiding new network users towards resources that help them to benefit immediately from network access.

Author: Jean Armour Polly
Author affiliation/institution: NYSERNet
Author E-mail: jpolly@nysernet.org
Author postal address: 111 College Place, Syracuse, NY 13244-4100
Author telephone number: (315) 443-4120

File format: Text
Number of files: One
Data format: Text
File size: 61KB, 1,361 lines

Primary/authoritative source: `ftp nysernet.org`
Instructions for access: `cd pub/resources/guides; ascii; get surf-ing.2.0.2.txt`
Additional sources/methods: Some other FTP sites

Last known revision date: December 1992
Number of revisions to date: Two major
First issue: 1992
Next planned revision/planned frequency of revision: 1993

Copyright restriction: "Copyright (c) 1992 Jean Armour Polly. Permission to reprint is granted for nonprofit educational purposes" (from the text).

Experience level: General.
Target audience: Mostly new network users.

Content sample:

BBS.OIT.UNC.EDU
Telnet to BBS.OIT.UNC.EDU or 152.2.22.80.
Type launch at the login message.
It's a must. Not only can you read Usenet Newsfeeds, but you can use LibTel, a scripted telnet gateway to access both U.S. and international libraries plus such things as Data Research Associates Library of Congress catalog, the Ham Radio Call Book, the National Science Foundation, the Weather Server, Webster's dictionary and thesaurus, and more.

Title: The Whole Internet
Resource Type: Book

The Whole Internet User's Guide & Catalog is one of several recent books on using the Internet. In addition to text for how to use the Internet and descriptions of several specific resources, the book includes a "catalog" of resources that is in a format quite similar to other resource guides. The catalog spans forty-six pages and includes over 200 resource listings organized by topic.

Author: Ed Krol
Author affiliation/institution: University of Illinois at Urbana-Champaign
Author E-mail: e-krol@uiuc.edu

Publisher: O'Reilly & Associates
Publisher postal address: 103 Morris St., Suite A, Sebastopol, CA 95472
ISBN: 1-56592-025-2

Cost: $29.95 (U.S.)

Number of pages: 400
Next planned revision/planned frequency of revision: Multiple editions are planned.

Copyright restriction: Copyright 1992 by O'Reilly & Associates, Inc. All rights reserved.

Experience level: Useful for beginning Internet users as a tutorial and to more experienced users as a reference tool.
Target audience: All Internet users
Environment applicability: Many examples are based on Unix, but most are applicable across computing platforms. The resources described may be accessed from any Internet site.

Content sample:

Reader's Guide to Periodical Literature

Yes, that old workhorse, the *Reader's Guide to Periodical Literature,* is available on the Internet. In case you've forgotten, it's a topic-oriented index to virtually all general-interest magazines published in the U.S.: *Time, Popular Mechanics,* and others. You can search it electronically, by author, title, subject, keyword, and so on.

Access via: telnet lib.uwstout.edu

Notes: O'Reilly has a Gopher and an anonymous FTP server that contains order information and other materials related to their books. Make a Gopher or anonymous FTP connection to gopher.ora.com or ftp.ora.com.

4
OPACs

Why Should a Library Make its Catalog Available to Everyone?

An OPAC is an Online Public Access Catalog, a library card catalog in electronic form. Many OPACs include additional capabilities, such as links to other databases and the ability to identify whether an item is on the library shelf. Some OPACs cover more than one library or can access the databases of other libraries, so you can find out what library has the book you are looking for, if the library you are using does not.

OPACs are some of the most useful resources on the Internet for researchers and scholars. They enable Internet users to find out about library collections all around the world and then use interlibrary loan to retrieve a book from the remote system. Some users employ the OPAC of a different institution because it is better suited for their search than the local system—for instance, one could browse a remote system for useful works, then use an author-title search on the local system to see whether they are available.

OPACs extend the reach of library users. They may decrease the need for interlibrary loan personnel to search for items if the patron has already identified a location where the item may be found. This semi-direct access to remote collections makes up somewhat for deficiencies in the local collection.

The obvious question is, why should a library make its OPAC available to people who are not local? The answer is, when a large number of libraries do so, all libraries benefit from the access, in exchange for sharing only a portion of the network OPAC users load. Your OPAC may see a slight increase in use, but your patrons suddenly have hundreds of other OPACs at their fingertips.

Currently, most Internet-accessible OPACs are located at universities and some large government institutions. Very few public libraries are represented. This is partially because universities are the most likely to have a preexisting Internet connection, partially because their size makes them the least likely to notice the increase in usage, and partially because their patrons are probably more likely to want access to so many other libraries. As the Z39.50 protocol for bibliographic interchange becomes standard with OPAC software sold by automation vendors, there will be an increase in the sharing of resources among libraries. Z39.50 enables a user to construct a query on his or her local OPAC and see if other OPACs have holdings that match the query—without needing to login directly to the remote OPAC.

Title: Accessing Online Bibliographic Databases
Resource Type: List

This is the most complete guide to OPACs currently available. Most OPACs are library card catalogs and many contain other databases or services. This list is international in scope and strives to contain all the OPACs listed elsewhere.

Author: Billy Barron
Author affiliation/institution: University of Texas at Dallas
Author E-mail: billy@utdallas.edu
File format: text, WordPerfect, or PostScript
Number of files: One for each form
Data format: Formatted list
Number of data items: Over 450
File size: Depends on the format. Ranges from 295KB (unformatted text) to 1.73MB (Post-Script).

Primary/authoritative source: `ftp ftp.unt.edu`
Instructions for access: `cd library;` `ls` and `get` to identify and transfer files.
Additional sources/methods: This is a fundamental component to the LIBS and Hytelnet software (in this chapter). Also available via FTP at several other sites.

Last known revision date: January 1993
Number of revisions to date: Several
First issue: 1990
Next planned revision/planned frequency of revision: Quarterly

Copyright restriction: "(C) 1989-1993 University of North Texas. Permission is granted to any individual or institution to use, copy, or distribute this document freely as long as it is not sold for profit. Excerpts from this document may be used in other documents provided they not sold for a profit. While every precaution has been taken in the preparation of this book, UNT and Billy Barron assumes no responsibility for errors or omissions, or for damages resulting from the use of the information herein" (From the directory cover page).

Target audience: General

Environment applicability: Almost all entries require telnet or tn3270 to access their content. Very few enable E-mail access. Some require registration prior to use.

Sample entry: Denmark's Library for Medicine and Science

Location: Denmark

To access:

1. Type TELNET COSMOS.BIB.DK.
2. At the Username prompt, type COSMOS.
3. For English, type DIA ENG.

To exit, type STOP.

Note: Billy Barron has recently moved from the University of North Texas to the University of Texas at Dallas, but the resource will remain at `ftp.unt.edu`.

Title: List of Contacts for Internet Online Bibliographic Databases
Resource Type: List

This list accompanies Accessing Online Bibliographic Databases (page 32). It includes contact information for the maintainers of many of the OPACs listed there. If things go wrong, these are the people to contact—however, a better first step will usually be your local system administrator.

Author: Billy Barron
Author affiliation/institution: University of Texas at Dallas
Author E-mail: billy@utdallas.edu

File format: Text
Number of files: One
Data format: Formatted list
Number of data items: Over 450.
File size: 20KB, 1,065 lines

Primary/authoritative source: `ftp ftp.unt.edu` (129.120.1.1)
Instructions for access: `cd library;` get `libraries.contacts.`
Additional sources/methods: none

Last known revision date: March 1993
Number of revisions to date: Unknown
First issue: Unknown
Next planned revision/planned frequency of revision: As new information becomes available

Copyright restriction: None

Target audience: System administrators, some end-users

Sample entry:

ALBA
    Forskningsbibliotekernes edb-kontor,
    (the national edp-office for the danish research libraries)
    Nyhavn 31 E,
    DK-1051 Copenhagen K,
    Denmark,
    Phone 33 93 46 33
    Fax 33 93 60 93.

Note: Billy Barron has recently moved to the University of Texas at Dallas from UNT. The fate of this resource may be uncertain.

Title: OPACs by Nation
Resource Type: Lists

Accessing Online Bibliographic Databases (this chapter) is now the most up-to-date listing of OPACs. This entry points to three other nations for which OPAC information exists. However, the data in the lists on this page are incorporated into Barron's guide. Additionally, none of the three lists have been updated since 1991.

Generally, a far better way to access OPACs in a particular country is to use Hytelnet or LIBS software (described in this chapter).

AARNet access to Australian and New Zealand OPACs. Compiled by Deidre E. Stanton <stanton@csuvax1.csu.murdoch.edu.au>. Available as ftp.unt.edu:pub/library/aarnet.library.

Canadian Internet Accessible Libraries. By John Sadler. Available as ftp.unt.edu:pub/library/canada.libs.

OPACs in the UK: A List of Interactive Library Catalogues on JANET. By the University of Sussex Library <Library@uk.ac.sussex.cluster>. Available as ftp.unt.edu:pub/library/uk.lib.

Title: Hytelnet
Resource Type: Software

Hytelnet is software for identifying and accessing OPACs, Free-Nets, BBSs, and other useful telnet-accessible sites and services. It is menu-driven and simple to use. The software is available for Amigas, PCs, Macintosh, Unix, and VMS. Some versions of the software (Unix and VMS) require someone with system administration skills to install.

Author: Peter Scott
Author affiliation/institution: University of Saskatchewan
Author E-mail: scottp@jester.usask.ca
Author telephone number: (306) 966-5920

File format: Text and executables
Number of files: One for each type of computer
Data format: Source code and data
File size: Varies for different types of computer

Primary/authoritative source: ftp access.usask.ca
Instructions for access: cd pub/hytelnet; use cd to go to the appropriate directory for the type of computer you want the software for, then use ls and get to retrieve those files.

Additional sources/methods: You may try the Unix client via `telnet access.usask.ca`. log on as `hytelnet`. The contact for this service is Earl Fogel <fogel@skyfox.usask.ca>.

Last known revision date: differs for different software. The PC software is the most heavily maintained, revised in February 1993.

Number of revisions to date: Six major

First issue: 1990

Next planned revision/planned frequency of revision: Quarterly

Copyright restriction: May not be incorporated into any commercial product or service. See the software distribution for further details.

Experience level: Some system administration skills are needed to install the software (varies for different software).

Target audience: General

Environment applicability: Operates in Unix and VMS environments only

Hytelnet menu (Unix version):

Welcome to HYTELNET version 6.4

What is HYTELNET?	<WHATIS>	
Library catalogs	<SITES1>	Up/Down arrow keys MOVE
Other resources	<SITES2>	Left/Right arrow keys SELECT
Help files for catalogs	<OP000>	
Catalog interfaces	<SYS000>	? for HELP anytime
Internet glossary	<GLOSSARY>	m returns to this screen
Telnet tips	<TELNET>	q quits
Key-stroke commands	<HELP>	

Notes: A paper about Hytelnet is available. Send this message to listserv@uhupvm1.uh.edu: `get scott prv3n4 f=mail`. This paper was published as part of The Public-Access Computer Systems Review, a LISTSERV mailing list that may be subscribed to by sending the message `subscribe pacs-p Your Name` to the address `listserv@uhupvm1.uh.edu`: (where `Your Name` is your real name, not your E-mail address).

A LISTSERV mailing list has been set up for people wishing to be informed of new versions of the program and announcements of new/updated/deleted files. To subscribe send a mail message to `listserv@kentvm.kent.edu` with the following in the body: `subscribe hytel-1 Your Name`.

Title: LIBS
Resource Type: Software

LIBS is software for identifying and accessing OPACs and other network-accessible re-sources. It is menu-driven and simple to use. An advantage over Hytelnet is that this soft-ware requires fewer system administration skills to get working—you just access it by FTP and run it. Otherwise, the contents are similar.

Author: Mark Resmer
Author affiliation/institution: Sonoma State University
Author E-mail: resmer@sonoma.edu
Author telephone number: (707) 664-2505

File format: Text
Number of files: One per platform. The Unix version is expanded with `tar` to 439 files be-fore executing.
Data format: Source code (data are embedded in the source code)
File size: 270KB (VMS version); 676KB (Unix version)

Primary/authoritative source: `ftp sonoma.edu`
Instructions for access: cd pub; binary; `ls` and `get` to identify and retrieve files.
`libs.com` is the VMS version, `libs.sh` is the Unix version.

Last known revision date: December 1992
Number of revisions to date: Unknown
First issue: Unknown
Next planned revision/planned frequency of revision: 1993

Copyright restriction: Copyright (c) 1991–92, Mark Resmer
Experience level: Minimal system administration skills are desirable to get the software working
Target audience: General
Environment applicability: Operates in VMS and Unix environments only

The LIBS main menu:

LIBS - Internet Access Software
Mark Resmer, Sonoma State University

On-line services available through the Internet:

1 United States Library Catalogs
2 Library Catalogs in other countries
3 Campus-wide Information Systems
4 Databases and Information Services
5 Wide-area Information Services
6 Information for first time users

Note: A paper on LIBS is available. Send this message to `list-serv@uhupvm1.uh.edu`: `get stanton prv3n4 f=mail`. This paper was published as part of The Public-Access Computer Systems Review, a LISTSERV mailing list that may be subscribed to by sending the message `subscribe pacs-p Your Name` to the address `listserv@uhupvm1.uh.edu`: (where `Your Name` is your real name, not your E-mail address).

5
E-mail, Mailing Lists, and Newsgroups

If This Seems Hard Now, Wait Until Everyone is on the Internet

This chapter includes listings for electronic mailing lists and Usenet newsgroups. These are the predominant means of communicating with people with whom you share a common interest. They are also one of the very fastest ways to identify an expert or groups of experts on a particular subject. The problem is that there are thousands of E-mail lists and newsgroups, and it is no small task to identify those in which you are most interested. Even after you identify some mailing lists to subscribe to, you might find yourself with hundreds of messages per week and no time to read them. Or, you might be even more disappointed to find that there is no discussion at all on a list of great appeal to you.

One of the things that Internet does is that it enables the formation of geographically dispersed communities. Once you are in touch with people who share your interests or vocation, your personal or professional contacts—and friends—can increase in number. The problem is not unlike your first day at a new school or a new job: There are hundreds or thousands of potential friends, but finding those who best match your interests and needs is a challenge. This chapter introduces some of the tools available to help you sift through all the available ongoing discussions to find those that have the most appeal for you. Chapter 8—Special Interest and Regional Resources—might help you to identify resources based on your particular interest or area of work.

This section covers the basics of mailing lists and newsgroups and then outlines netiquette—rules for interacting with people when using computer-mediated communication. Then discussed are some methods for finding the E-mail address of someone whose name you know.

Mailing Lists and Newsgroups

Electronic mailing lists are single email addresses that point to multiple people. When you send mail to a mailing list, you use a single E-mail address. The address is connected to software that distributes your message to all subscribers of the mailing list. There is quite a bit of variability in how lists are maintained and what constitutes appropriate discussion topics and methods. Some lists allow subscribers only to send E-mail, and might also prohibit subscription without an invitation. Many use automatic software to allow subscription and unsubscription. The number of people on a list might be fewer than ten or greater than 5,000, with anywhere from five messages per year to over fifty messages per day. The length and content of the messages also vary across different mailing lists.

LISTSERV is a popular mailserver and mailing list maintainer. It is a program that runs on IBM mainframes running the CMS operating system. LISTSERV reads incoming mail and processes simple commands that enable people to subscribe and unsubscribe to mailing lists, retrieve files, or search the archives of mailing lists. Other mailing list software exists, most of which is fairly similar in syntax to LISTSERV. Some mailing lists require a person to add or remove subscribers.

Newsgroups contain the subdivided content of Usenet, also known as Netnews. Usenet is a distributed worldwide electronic bulletin board system. Instead of each message going to each subscriber, as occurs with mailing lists, messages are distributed to the thousands of Usenet hosts—using transport mechanisms similar in concept to the mailing list (but not similar in implementation). Usenet readers read the newsgroups they are interested in with software that accesses a local Usenet server. This is in many ways a more efficient method for communicating with people on a given topic than a mailing list because only one copy of each message is needed for an institution. In addition, the software used to interact with Usenet newsgroups is almost always better than E-mail software for sorting through large numbers of Usenet articles (also known as posts or postings).

Mailing lists and newsgroups have different personalities based on their content, their readers' interests, the number of messages, and the level of diversity in the readership. All other things being equal, the Usenet interface and transport mechanisms allow for more of a conversational atmosphere—people are more likely to respond to specific portions of a previous post or to engage in side conversations. With a mailing list, every subscriber gets every single message sent to the list, so off-topic conversations or personal notes tend to be frowned upon, as are long digressions or even lengthy messages. These are generalities, though. Investigate individual mailing lists and newsgroups and you will find there is quite a bit of variation among them, regardless of the method by which they are distributed.

E-mail for Communication

Electronic mail is the lowest-common-denominator for computer networked communication. Regardless of which type of network someone is connected to, it is a sure thing that you can exchange email messages with him or her, provided that there exists a gateway or series of gateways from your network to theirs. A gateway is a computer which is connected to two or more networks simultaneously, and can pass messages between them.

One of the most common gateways for Internet users is the BITNET-to-Internet gateway. In fact, there are hundreds of machines that can serve this purpose: Almost all machines running LISTSERV are connected to both networks. Only a few years ago, you might have needed to know the explicit gateway addresses to get from one network to another. Now, you frequently can use an Internet-style address for the gateway machine, with no need to worry about the specifics. For example, an Internet user might send E-mail to a BITNET address with this syntax:

```
To: username@node.bitnet
```

Rather than the explicitly gatewayed address:

```
To: username%node@cunyvm.cuny.edu
```

(where cunyvm.cuny.edu is a well-known BITNET-to-Internet gateway). The most complete description of how to get from one network to another may be found in Frey & Adams' *!%@: A Directory of Electronic Mail Addressing and Networks* (page 110).

When you read E-mail lists or newsgroups, you will encounter people from all over the world who might not be part of the Internet. You will see many readers from UUNet (a Unix-based network on which Usenet was originally based), FIDONet (a PC-to-PC network which minimizes the cost for users; often used to connect local BBSs to each other), BITNET, and commercial services such as CompuServe, among others. (Quarterman's *The Matrix* (page 111) is the authoritative listing of networks and network contacts, although it is somewhat dated.) This means that although the mailing list or newsgroup might be accessible by readers using many types of networks, you can not make assumptions about what else they have—non-Internet users might not have the capability to use ftp or telnet or they might be paying money to read everything on the group. Although English is the most common language on these forums, it is by no means the only language.

Netiquette for Mailing Lists and Newsgroups

"Do to others what you would have them do to you" is probably the best summary of how to be a good network citizen. For mailing lists and newsgroups, the people who are subscribed make up a sub-culture, which has its own history, morals, and values. Become familiar with what's going on in a particular forum before jumping in. This is the same sort of behavior which you would engage in without thinking, were you to walk into a room where a conversation was taking place among people you didn't know. With computer networks, though, it's so easy to just send a note to the list that people do not always take the time to get their bearings before plunging into the conversation. Read the FAQ (page 57), if there is one. Follow the discussion for a day or maybe a week.

Another way to get information about a list is to access the archives. Unfortunately, this is not as easy as it should be. Not all newsgroups and mailing lists are archived, and the archives might not be easy to access. FTP sites or software such as LISTSERV might enable you to find out what has been said recently—perhaps you'll find an answer to a question you were going to ask in the archives. Do not get discouraged if you do all of the above and finally send a note to the folks on the mailing list and are told something to the effect of, "we just discussed that last week and we don't want to discuss it again." With thousands of new network users every month, and dozens of new mailing lists and newsgroups being created each week, some repetitiveness will occur in every forum. Try to remember this when you're an old dog on the mailing list.

Last words of advice for subscribing to mailing lists: in absolutely no mailing list will you send a request to `subscribe` to the list address itself. There is always a method for subscribing that involves sending to another address. Sometimes this is an address such as `listserv` or `server` or `majordomo` at the same node as the mailing list, other times you add `-request` to the name of the list and send to that address. Sometimes there is a human who makes the list additions and deletions, other times it's automatic. Be patient if there's a human involved for there might be a delay of a day or two to get subscribed. Unsubscribing is not always easy, either. Sometimes there are variations in the E-mail address for you that the remote site sees, so that you can not unsubscribe using the automatic software. Don't pester the list subscribers with this—instead, consult the message you received when you subscribed or heard about the list and contact the list manager. The folks on the mailing list can not help to unsubscribe you, so there's usually no point in sending your plea to the list. Keep any information you get when subscribing, so that you know who the list manager is and how to unsubscribe later.

White Pages E-mail Directories

There are several different methods for discovering the E-mail address of an individual. Currently, there is no effort underway to construct one single directory of E-mail for the entire Internet. This is because of the high mobility of individuals, the tendency for institutions to change machine names, and (perhaps mostly) the large number of names involved.

Several methods exist for finding the E-mail address of somebody. If all else fails, a snail-net (slang for the regular postal service) note or telephone call may be your only recourse.

Finger

Finger is perhaps the simplest way to find an E-mail address, but it also the least likely to be successful. Finger works over Internet only, and is not available under CMS, MVS, or PROFS. To finger someone, you specify their email address, for example:

```
finger newby@uiuc.edu
```

This command will return information about that username, if it is available. If you get the Internet node wrong, or the wrong characters in the username you are finger-ing, you may get no results. In some cases, the finger command will access a campus-wide E-mail directory. In others, it will look through the usernames available on the machine at which you direct your finger command. In most cases, it will simply see if there is a user of that exact username on that particular Internet node.

As a guess, if you know someone's institution you can try to finger the generic institution name. So, if you know somebody at MIT, and you have seen E-mail from addresses such as "so-and-so@athena.mit.edu" you can try:

```
finger username@mit.edu
```

Sometimes, there is no such node. Other times you will get a helpful message. You can also try fingering the username `help`, which will occasionally result in a useful response.

Some nodes allow for more than just a username in a finger command, for example:

```
finger "greg newby"@uiuc.edu
```

Nameservers

Several different types of nameservers exist, some of which are peculiar to one institution. The CSO nameserver (developed at the University of Illinois) is perhaps the closest to a standard, representing about fifty percent of all nameservers available via Gopher.

Gopher is the best path to looking up people when you know their institution, if the institution has made their nameserver available as a Gopher database. In a few cases, institutions might have chosen not to make their nameserver available to the public, but this is not very likely because the nameserver software is generally intended to enable people to find out email and other information about institutional members.

In Gopherspace, nameservers usually fall under directories labeled `Phone Books`.

WHOIS

There are a growing number of WHOIS servers across the Internet. These sometimes have the advantage of containing listings of people from more than one institution. WHOIS was first started by the U.S. Defense Department's Network Information Center (NIC) at `nic.ddn.mil`. They are a source for free WHOIS software (ftp to `nic.ddn.mil`).

Originally, the DoD NIC wanted to be the source for white pages listings for all of the Internet (at least the U.S. part of the Internet). However, they have abandoned that plan and now their WHOIS server only contains contact information for network administrators and other key personnel at institutions or hosts on Internet. Many institutions have created their own WHOIS server for use as an Internet-accessible phone book.

You can interact with WHOIS servers using client software, via E-mail, with finger, or through Gopher.

X.500

X.500 is a nameservice standard that is currently used most heavily in Europe. The layered transport model of Open Systems Integration (OSI) makes this more complete than standard finger. For people on the U.S. portion of the Internet, the best available method to look for someone using X.500 is via the Gopher-X.500 gateway. X.500 includes descriptive information about institutions, departments, individuals, and networks in plain language, instead of the cryptic combination of usernames and Internet node names that are the basis of finger.

Title: WHOIS Servers and Gopher links
Resource Type: List

WHOIS is one method for finding an individual's E-mail address, or for getting information about a particular Internet node. WHOIS databases may be searched by client software or though a Gopher gateway. Each WHOIS database is maintained by its host institution.

Maintainer: Matt Power
Maintainer affiliation/institution: Massachusetts Institute of Technology

Maintainer E-mail: mhpower@athena.mit.edu

File format: Text
Number of files: Two
Data format: List
File size: 18KB, 812 lines (Gopher list); 11KB, 342 lines (WHOIS servers list)

Primary/authoritative source: `ftp sipb.mit.edu`
Instructions for access: `cd /pub/whois; get whois-servers.list` or `get whois-servers.gopher-links`
Additional sources/methods: Search directly through Gopher. WHOIS servers are usually found on the `Phone Book` menu item.
Last known revision date: March 1993
First issue: Unknown
Next planned revision/planned frequency of revision: As new servers become known.

Copyright restriction: (from the text) "If you redistribute this list, or excerpt a significant number of entries from it, be sure to also pass along the original anonymous-FTP location, and request that updates be sent to my e-mail address, as specified at the top of this file."

Experience level: WHOIS searches can sometimes be tricky and return unexpected results.
Target audience: General

Content sample: (from `whois-servers.gopher-links`)

Name=Corporation for National Research Initiatives, Knowbot interface C=US
Type=w
Port=43
Path=
Host=nri.reston.va.us

Note: The client software for WHOIS resides at the same Internet host and several others. It was written by the DDN's NIC and is also available from `nic.ddn.mil`.

Title: Directory of Scholarly Electronic Conferences
Resource Type: List

This list of over 1,200 mailing lists solves one of the largest problems with the Internet: there is too much available information, and it is difficult to narrow things down. Diane Kovacs has put together lists of mailing lists that may appeal to people in various disciplines and arranged the disciplines alphabetically. This enables you to search a much smaller number of mailing lists to find the one in which you are interested.

Editor: Diane Kovacs, Editor in Chief, and others
Editor affiliation/institution: Kent State University
Editor email: dkovacs@kentvm.kent.edu

Editor USPS address: Kent State University Libraries, Kent, OH 44242
Editor telephone number: (216) 672-3045

File formats: Text for general use and binhexed MS Word for Macintosh
Number of files: Thirteen
Data format: formatted list with labeled fields, or Hypercard stack
File size: from 26KB to 360KB each

Primary/authoritative source: `ftp ksuvxa.kent.edu`
Instructions for access: `cd library; ls` and `get` to choose files
Additional sources/methods: Via E-mail to listserv@kentvm.kent.edu. Send the commands `index` and/or `get` to identify and retrieve desired files (e.g., `get acadlist readme`).
Last known revision date: February 1993
Number of revisions to date: Unknown
First issue: Unknown
Next planned revision/planned frequency of revision: Quarterly

Copyright restriction (from ACADLIST.README): Copyright 1992 by Diane K. Kovacs, The Directory Team and Kent State University Libraries. Single copies of this directory from its networked sources, or of specific entries from their networked sources, may be made for internal purposes, personal use, or study by an individual, an individual library, or an educational or research institution. The directory or its contents may not be otherwise reproduced or republished in excerpt or in entirety, in print or electronic form, without permission from Diane K. Kovacs, Kent State University Libraries.

Target audience: People in academic environments.
Environment applicability: Anyone can use the text versions of files. Macintosh users may find the binhexed files easier to read and more attractive for printing.

Contents (from ACADLIST README):

ACADLIST README   (explanatory notes for the Directory)
ACADSTAC.HQX   (binhexed, self-decompressing, HYPERCARD Stack of first 7 files - Keyword searchable)
ACADCOMP.HQX   (binhexed, self-decompressing, HYPERCARD Stack of FILE8 - Keyword searchable)
ACADLIST FILE1   (Anthropology- Education) 53k
ACADLIST FILE2   (Geography-Library and Information Science) 91k
ACADLIST FILE3   (Linguistics-Political Science) 49k
ACADLIST FILE4   (Psychology-Writing) 54k
ACADLIST FILE5   (Biological Sciences) 43k
ACADLIST FILE6   (Physical Sciences) 43k
ACADLIST FILE7   (Business, Academia, News)
ACADLIST FILE8   (Computer Science, Social, Cultural, and Political Aspects of Computing and Academic Computing Support)

ACADWHOL HQX   (binhexed self-decompressing Macintosh M.S. Word 4.0 document
                of all 8 files)
ACADLIST.CHANGES (this is now empty due to difficulty of keeping up with the chang-
                es this time.)

Note: A printed version that combines this list with Michael Strangelove's Electronic Journals list is available as a book from the Association of Research Libraries. See complete information on pages 58–59.

Title: Interest Groups List of Mailing Lists
Resource Type: List

This is a key resource for identifying mailing lists on all topics. The list contains over 800
entries for mailing lists around the world. Some lists are maintained by LISTSERV or other
automatic software, others are maintained "by hand." In all cases it is necessary to send to
an address other than the mailing list address to subscribe or unsubscribe!

Maintainer: Vivian Neou
Maintainer affiliation/institution: Network Information Systems Center at SRI International
Maintainer E-mail: vivian@nisc.sri.com
Corporate postal address: 333 Ravenswood Avenue, Menlo Park, CA 94025
Corporate telephone number: (415) 859-4781

File format: Text or compressed text
Number of files: One (but will be sent in multiple parts if requested via E-mail)
Data format: Formatted list
File size: 1.01MB, 126K lines

Primary/authoritative source: `ftp ftp.nisc.sri.com`
Instructions for access: `cd netinfo; get interest-groups` (or `get inter-
est-groups.Z`)
Additional sources/methods: May be requested via email. Send a message to `mail-
server@nisc.sri.com` with the text `send netinfo/interest-groups` (you
may send a `help` message for further information).

Last known revision date: September 1992
Number of revisions to date: Unknown
First issue: Unknown
Next planned revision/planned frequency of revision: Quarterly

Copyright restriction: None

Target audience: General. There is a list for virtually any topic. Many are non-English.
Environment applicability: E-mail is required to subscribe to and receive any mailing list.

Notes: To keep informed of new lists as they are announced subscribe to the LISTSERV mailing list `new-list@ndsuvm1.bitnet`.

Some mailing lists are gatewayed to Usenet. Currently, only about 100 are available this way, but as more mailing lists are made accessible via Usenet the easier software interface might make for different types of communication via mailing lists—communication without such a need to keep traffic to a manageable minimum.

An indexed version is available as a book (updated annually): *Internet: Mailing Lists* published by Prentice Hall. ISBN number 0-13-327941-3. A version of this list is available as a machine-readable database and HyperCard stack via FTP to `dartcms1.dartmouth.edu;` `cd siglists;` use `ls` and `get` to view files. (This is a CMS site. You must give the command `cd siglists` before `ls` or `get` will work.) Last updated March 1993, the list does not match `interest-groups.txt` exactly in content.

Title: Listserv Lists
Resource Type: List

LISTSERV software runs on IBM mainframes. It is the standard for automatic networked mailing list management. LISTSERV was first developed for use with BITNET, but works at least as well for Internet. Current LISTSERV software is smart enough to route a message via BITNET or Internet, depending on which way is most likely to get to a desired recipient faster.

Interaction with LISTSERV is via email for Internet users. BITNET users may also send commands "interactively" through the line-at-a-time method for sending messages (on IBM mainframes, this is accomplished with the TELL command. On VMS, it's send). There are about 280 copies of LISTSERV running worldwide. Because all the LISTSERV-ers know about each other, any one of them can generate the list of currently available public mailing lists managed by LISTSERV.

Please see the summary of how to subscribe/unsubscribe and get help from LISTSERV below.

Author: Eric Thomas
Author Affiliation/institution: L'Ecole Polytechnic
Author E-mail: eric@cearn.bitnet

File formats: Text
Number of files: One
Data format: Formatted list with single-line entries
File size: 3,725 lines, 257KB

Primary/authoritative source: Any LISTSERV
Instructions for access: Send an E-mail message to the nearest LISTSERV username with the text `list global`. You will get a response, usually within a few minutes (depending on time of day and network load). The LISTSERV username at the University of Illi-

nois is `listserv@vmd.cso.uiuc.edu` (or `listserv@uiucvmd.bitnet`). A central node for the United States is `listserv@cunyvm.cuny.edu`. For Europe, a central node is `listserv@cearn.earn.ch`.
Additional sources/methods: None

Last known revision date: Unknown
Number of revisions to date: Unknown
First issue: Unknown
Next planned revision/planned frequency of revision: Immediately and automatically as mailing lists are added or discontinued
Copyright restriction: None

Target audience: LISTSERV mailing lists cover all topics.
Environment applicability: Anyone from any network can subscribe to a LISTSERV mailing list, provided LISTSERV can identify your return address as valid.

Notes: The entries are a single line each, including the mailing list address and a brief description.
Be careful when subscribing to LISTSERV mailing lists. The method is always the same:

1. Find the address for the list you desire.
2. Send this message to the username `listserv@node` (where "node" is the node where the list address is.)

        subscribe listname Your Name

where listname is the name of the list, and Your Name is your true name, not your E-mail address. For example, to subscribe to `virtu-l@vmd.cso.uiuc.edu`, I would send this message to `listserv@vmd.cso.uiuc.edu`:

        subscribe virtu-l Gregory B. Newby

3. You will get a note of acknowledgment.
4. To unsubscribe, just send this message to the same `listserv` address:

        unsubscribe listname

5. You never ever need to send your subscribe or unsubscribe command to the mailing list address! This will just have the effect of broadcasting your request to the entire mailing list, who will not be able to subscribe you.

6. LISTSERV will send you a help file. Just send a message to any LISTSERV address with the text `help` (LISTSERV ignores subject lines).

7. LISTSERV also manages files and keeps archives of many mailing lists. Send an `index` command to find out about these.

Title: Publicly Accessible Mailing Lists
Resource Type: List

This is the list of Internet and UUNET-based mailing lists. There is some overlap with the Interest Groups List (page 51) and no overlap with LISTSERV Lists (page 52). Most of these mailing lists are maintained "by hand," which means that a human response is needed for every request to be added or removed from the list. The majority are not archived, but some are archived by the Unix "listserv" software or have FTP-accessible archives (the Unix "listserv" software is unrelated but similar in function to the LISTSERV software which runs on IBM mainframe computers). Check with the list maintainer, whose E-mail address is included in every mailing list entry in the file.

The best place to get these lists is to read the Usenet newsgroup `news.announce.newusers`. The current version should always be available.

Maintainer: Stephanie da Silva
Maintainer E-mail: arielle@taronga.com

File format: Text
Number of files: Four
Data format: Formatted list
File size: 104KB, 2,502 lines, 491 entries

Primary/authoritative source: `news.announce.newusers` (Usenet newsgroup)
Instructions for access: read the newsgroup
Additional sources/methods: FTP archives of `news.announce.newusers`. These include: `pitmanager.mit.edu:pub/usenet/news.announce.newusers/Publicly_Accessible_Mailing_Lists,_Part_[1234].Z` and others worldwide (use Archie for a current listing).

Last known revision date: March 1993
Number of revisions to date: Unknown
First issue: Unknown
Next planned revision/planned
Frequency of revision: as new information becomes available. The current list is posted every two weeks to `news.announce.newusers`.

Copyright restriction: None

Target audience: Diverse, there are many different topics for the mailing lists, many of which are oriented towards hobbies or personal interests.

Content sample:

bagpipe
  Contact: pipes-request@sunapee.dartmouth.edu

Purpose: Any topic related to bagpipes, most generally defined as any instrument where air is forced manually from a bellows or bag through drones and/or over reeds. All manner of Scottish, Irish, English, and other instruments are discussed. Anyone with an interest is welcome.

Title: Active Usenet Newsgroups
Resource Type: List

This is the most complete list of Usenet newsgroups available. It includes many regional newsgroups and all of the groups from the alt. hierarchy. Only currently active newsgroups are included, not dormant ones. It is difficult to pick interesting newsgroups based only on their name. This list also includes the one-line description for each newsgroup to make the list easier for searching.

Author: Lou Bona
Author Affiliation/institution: Stockton State College, Pomona, NJ
Author E-mail: bona@pilot.njin.net
File formats: Text
Number of files: One
Data format: Single-line alphabetical entries
File size: 230KB, 4,883 lines

Primary/authoritative source: Read news.announce.newusers
Additional sources/methods: `ftp pilot.njin.net; cd pub/Internet-course; get enews.lst`

Last known revision date: August 1992
Number of revisions to date: One
First issue: August 1992
Next planned revision/planned frequency of revision: Unknown

Copyright restriction: None

Environment applicability: Access to a Usenet site and news software is required. Currently, these are most often found with Unix hosts, but might also be available for VMS hosts. Free-Net sites and some BBS may also give Usenet access.

Sample entry:

sci.virtual-worlds Modeling the universe. (Moderated)

Notes: Lou compiled this list while in a class on networking. It will probably not be maintained! Because several new newsgroups are created every week, this list will rapidly become outdated. However, the list's inclusion of newsgroups from many national and regional domains makes it more useful than other lists.

Speak to your system administrator about adding a newsgroup that you desire. Usually, there is no difficulty and little overhead in doing this.

You may obtain a list of currently available newsgroups at your own site. The easiest way to do this with a Unix host is to run the Usenet software (e.g., nn or rn) and then view a file called .newsrc, in which all currently available newsgroups will be listed by name only.

Moderated newsgroups, for which posted materials go to a moderator for approval rather than immediately to the newsgroup, are indicated as "(Moderated)."

Title: news.announce.newusers
Resource Type: Usenet newsgroup

This newsgroup is a must read for any new Usenet reader. It is also a reference of first resort for experienced readers. There are a relatively small number (about thirty) of articles re-posted every week. Topics include netiquette, getting started, lists of mailing lists and newsgroups, Usenet descriptions, and rules for posting.

Author: Several
Author Affiliation/institution: Several
Author email: Included in each article

File format: Text
Number of files: Several dozen
Data format: Text, some with lists or bibliographic references
File size: Varies from under 100 to several thousand lines

Primary/authoritative source: `news.announce.newusers`
Instructions for access: Use your local news reading software, such as `nn`, `rn`, or Anu-News.
Additional sources/methods: `ftp pit-manager.mit.edu ; cd pub/usenet/news.announce.newusers` and use `ls` or `get` to retrieve particular articles.

Next planned revision/planned frequency of revision: Most are revised every few months.

Copyright restriction: most may be freely distributed

Experience level: Novice
Target audience: A must read for all new users of Usenet

Content sample: (from *Emily Postnews Answers Your Questions on Netiquette,* a satirical piece by Gene Spafford <spaf@cs.purdue.edu>)

Q: How should I pick a subject for my articles?

A: Keep it short and meaningless. That way people will be forced to actually read your article to find out what's in it. This means a bigger audience for you, and we all know that's what the net is for. If you do a followup, be sure and keep the same subject, even if it's totally meaningless and not part of the same discussion. If you don't, you won't catch all the people who are looking for stuff on the original topic, and that means less audience for you.

Title: news.answers
Resource Type: Usenet Newsgroup

This newsgroup re-posts all of the FAQs from all other newsgroups. FAQs are "Frequently Asked Questions." These are the first stop for the user who is wondering whether the people on a mailing list can answer a question she has, or who wants to know what topics are under discussion. Some FAQs are better than others, but one fact emerges from all of them: There is expertise accessible in Usenet newsgroups which can not be found elsewhere.

Authors: Many
Author Affiliation/institution: Many
Author E-mail: Included in each FAQ

File format: Text
Number of files: Several hundred
Data format: Text, some with lists or bibliographic references
File size: Varies from under 100 to several thousand lines

Primary/authoritative source: `news.answers`
Instructions for access: Use your local news reading software, such as `nn`, `rn`, or `Anu-News`.
Additional sources/methods:

1. FAQs are kept in the archives for individual newsgroups (if they have an archive). Use Archie to find these or (better) consult the newsgroup itself.

2. `pit-manager.mit.edu` keeps most of the FAQs available via anonymous FTP. `cd pub/usenet/news.answers` and use `ls` or `get` to retrieve the FAQs for a particular newsgroup.

Next planned revision/planned frequency of revision: most FAQs are revised frequently, from every week to every few months.

Copyright restriction: Most may be freely distributed

Experience level: Some assume familiarity with the subject matter.
Target audience: Anyone who is considering asking a question of a newsgroup's readership.
Environment applicability: Although FAQs are primarily directed at the Usenet audience, much of the information contained in them may be applied generally.

Content sample: (from >rec.games.chess Answers to Frequently Asked Questions by William R. Shauck <shauck@netcom.com>)

[1] Federation Internationale des Echecs (FIDE)

FIDE (pronounced "fee-day") is an international chess organization that organizes tournaments (e.g. Olympiad), grants titles, and controls the World Championship cycle. Write to: Federation Internationale des Echecs, Abendweg 1, P.O. Box 2841, CH-6002 Lucerne, Switzerland. Phone 041 41 513378,9; fax 041 41 515846.

FIDE grants three over-the-board titles: FIDE Master (FM), International Master (IM), and International Grandmaster (IGM; but more commonly just "Grandmaster" and "GM"). FM can be obtained by keeping your FIDE rating over 2300 for 25 games. IM and GM titles require performances at certain levels for 25-30 games (2450 for IM and 2600 for GM). This is usually achieved by obtaining several "norms." A norm is obtained when a player makes at least a given score in a FIDE tournament. The required score is a function of the number of rounds and the strength of the opposition. There are also minimum rating requirements. There are about 35 GM's, 60 IM's, and 100 FM's living in the United States, not all of whom are active players.

Title: Directory of Electronic Journals and Newsletters
Resource Type: List

This is an authoritative listing of electronic journals and newsletters. It complements Kovac's listing of academic mailing lists (pages 49–51).

Author: Michael Strangelove
Author Affiliation/institution: University of Ottawa
Author E-mail: 441495@acadvm1.uottawa.ca
Author postal address: Religious Studies Department, 177 Waller, Ottawa, Ontario, K1N 6N5, Canada
Author telephone number: (613) 747-0642

File format: Text
Number of files: One or two, depending on source
Data format: Plain and formatted text, plus indexes
File size: 243KB, 6,901 lines total

Primary/authoritative source: `email to listserv@acadvm1.uottawa.ca`
Instructions for access: Send this message (note spelling)

```
send ejournl1 directry
send ejournl2 directry
```

Additional sources/methods: Several anonymous FTP sites carry this listing, including `sunsite.unc.edu` as `/pub/academic/library/libsoft/ ejournals.txt`

Last known revision date: July 1992
Number of revisions to date: Two major
First issue: 1992
Next planned revision/planned frequency of revision: Annually

Copyright restriction: "This Directory is intended for free dissemination as long as this header remains intact. The compilation as a whole is Copyright (C) by Michael Strangelove, 1991. All rights reserved. Permission is hereby granted for non commercial use by electronic bulletin board/conference systems, individuals and libraries. All commercial use requires the permission of the author. The Association of Research Libraries is the only authorized not-for-profit distributor of print copies of the Directory of Electronic Journals and Newsletters." (from the text)

Content sample:

>>> PSYCOLOQUY <<<

PSYCOLOQUY is a refereed electronic journal (ISSN 1044-0143) sponsored American Psychological Association's Science Directorate and Office of Publication and Communication and co-edited by Stevan Harnad (Psychology Department, Princeton University) and Perry London (Dean, Graduate School of Applied and Professional Psychology, Rutgers University).

PSYCOLOQUY publishes brief reports of ideas and findings on which the author wishes to solicit rapid peer feedback, international and interdisciplinary ("Scholarly Skywriting"), in all areas of psychology and its related fields (biobehavioral, cognitive, neural, social, etc.). All contributions are refereed by members of PSYCOLOQUY's 60-member Editorial Board.

Notes: A printed version which combines this list of electronic journals with Diane Kovac's ACADLIST listing of email lists is available as a book from the Association of Research Libraries. A third edition should be available in early to mid-1993. The book is called Directory of Electronic Journals, Newsletters and Academic Discussion Lists 2nd ed. by Michael Strangelove & Diane Kovacs. 1992. 241 p.; ISSN: 1057-1337. To order contact:

Office of Scientific & Academic Publishing
Association of Research Libraries
1527 New Hampshire Avenue, NW
Washington, DC 20036 USA
ARLHQ@UMDC.BITNET; (202) 232-2466 (voice); (202) 462-7849 (fax)

A third edition will become available in 1993 in both print and electronic form. The third edition will be larger than the second.

6
Resources for Anyone

Some Things Are for Everybody

It takes awhile for most new Internet users to identify something of immediate use to them. People hear about the Internet and are told stories of how some day the world will be connected by a data superhighway, but that does not translate directly into something which they can find that really makes the Internet better than, say, a newspaper or the telephone.

This chapter includes some resources that might help a new Internet user to know just what there is that he or she could really use. The resources are special in that they have a very wide audience and a large range of applicability.

For new Internet users, this chapter might constitute a "first stop." Gopher also makes a good first immersive experience, but it can quickly leave one with a feeling of being overwhelmed. Instead, perhaps the new user would like to know the temperature and forecast for the city in which a friend lives. Or, maybe a search of the ERIC database for a current citation on a topic. Campus-Wide Information Systems (CWIS) are sometimes as overwhelming as Gopher, but some users might find the information contained in them much less alien.

The few resources in this chapter might not be the ones you would choose to introduce to a new user. Think about the ones you would like to show to new users with particular backgrounds, then go ahead and do it.

Title: CWIS List (Campus-Wide Information Systems)
Resource Type: List

Campus-Wide Information Systems (CWIS) are used by academic institutions to provide information to their students and staff. Most CWIS applications have information which is generally useful to people outside of the immediate academic community, making them a valuable Internet resource. The software, hardware, and log-on instructions are all different — the *CWIS List* can tell you how to log on to each one directly. In some cases, you will be better served to access a CWIS through another tool. LIBS, Gopher, and Hytelnet are examples of software packages that can link you directly to a CWIS without you having to know all the specific log-on information.

Maintainer: Judy Hallman
Author affiliation/institution: Office of Information Technology, University of North Carolina at Chapel Hill
Author E-mail: Judy_Hallman@unc.edu
Author USPS address: OIT, 311 Wilson Library 0254A, CB#3460, University of North

Carolina at Chapel Hill, Chapel Hill, NC 27514.
Author telephone number: (919) 962-9107

File formats: Text
Number of files: One
Data format: Text
File size: 42KB, 1,861 lines.

Primary/authoritative source: `ftp sunsite.unc.edu`
Instructions for access: `cd pub/docs/about-the-net; get cwis-l`
Additional sources/methods: Various other FTP sites. Posted periodically to mailing lists such as `CWIS-L@wuvmd.wustl.edu` and `PACS-L@uhupvml.uh.edu` (both are LISTSERV lists).

Last known revision date: November 1992
Number of revisions to date: Several
First issue: 1991
Next planned revision/planned frequency of revision: 1993

Copyright restriction: None

Target audience: CWISs have many different types of information. Most have quite a bit that might be relevant to people not on the campus that supplies the CWIS.

Content sample:

> Dalhousie University Computing & Information Services
> ac.dal.ca (129.173.1.100)
> Username: dalinfo
> Hardware/Software: Uses pnn software
> Contact: dalinfo@ac.dal.ca
> Information provided by: Peter Scott <scott@sklib.usask.ca>

Notes: This file may not be up to date. You will usually have an easier time browsing CWISs through Gopher, Hytelnet, LIBS, or through another menu-driven program (many BBS and CWISs might lead you to other CWISs).

Title: ERIC Bibliographic Database
Resource Type: Database

ERIC is a large bibliographic database. It is directed primarily at educators, but there are materials on a large number of topics that are peripheral to education. Its database quality and large scope make it a database of choice for almost any search topic. There are three publicized access points on Internet for ERIC. You can probably also access ERIC locally in a library, either on CD-ROM or on paper.

Author: ERIC (Educational Resources Information Center)
Author Affiliation/institution: Department of Education
Author E-mail: eric@suvm.acs.syr.edu
Author USPS address: ERIC Clearinghouse on Information Resources, Syracuse University, Syracuse, NY13244-2340.
Author telephone number: (315) 443-3640 (v); (315) 443-5448 (f)
Author alternate telephone number: 1(800) LET-ERIC

File formats: Indexed file managed by SPIRES and PRISM software. Contains full bibliographic citations plus abstracts. Full text of many materials may be obtained on paper or microfiche from ERIC (ordering information is available online).
Data format: Text only
File size: Online data are from 1984 and include 263,239 records through 1992.

Primary/authoritative source: `telnet acsnet.syr.edu` (128.230.1.21)
Instructions for access:

1. When connected, you will probably need to press the return key several times
2. At the > prompt, type `SUINFO` (case insensitive)
3. Select a terminal type (vt100, usually)
4. Use the tab or arrow keys on your keyboard to advance to the `COMMAND` prompt. Type `SUINFO` and press return.
5. Follow instructions. ERIC is part of the `General Interest` menu option.
6. Type `logoff` at any prompt to exit the system.

Additional sources/methods:

Method A: Auburn University, accessed via `tn3270 auducacd.duc.auburn.edu` (131.204.2.13).

1. Use the tab or arrow keys on your keyboard to advance to the `APPLICATION` prompt. Type `01` and press return.
2. At the main menu, type `eric`
3. Follow instructions to search
4. Type Q or `Quit` to log off

Method B: University of Saskatchewan Library System, accessed via telnet sklib.usask.ca (128.233.1.20)

1. At the `USERNAME` prompt type `sonia`
2. Select `Education Databases`
3. Select `ERIC`
4. Follow instructions to search, use help for assistance
5. Type Q or `Quit` to exit ERIC, then type `Quit` again to log off

Last known revision date: Fourth quarter 1992
Number of revisions to date: Quarterly since 1984

First issue: Public availability announced in September 1992
Next planned revision/planned frequency of revision: quarterly updates. New items are added, old items remain.
Cost: The online system is free. There is a charge for full-text documents ordered from ERIC.
Copyright restriction: None

Experience level: General
Target audience: Although the ERIC database is directed primarily at educators it contains a very wide-ranging content. It is a database of choice for almost any general information need.

Notes: I have listed Syracuse University as the primary access point for ERIC because they are the publisher of *ERIC Networker,* a periodic electronic update on how to access ERIC via Internet (posted to the *NETTRAIN* and *PACS-L* LISTSERV mailing lists, among other places. Also available on request via E-mail to eric@suvm.acs.syr.edu). The Auburn and Saskatchewan access points contain similar (but not identical) coverage for the ERIC database and may offer quicker or easier service, depending on user experience and purpose. The interfaces are different, too.

The ERIC Clearinghouse on Information Resources is not the producer of the ERIC database; they are one of sixteen clearinghouses and a central administration infrastructure that produces the database.

For details on copyright status of ERIC and distribution methods, contact the executive director of ERIC: Robert Stonehill, rsn@nihcu.gov.

Many libraries hold the entire ERIC document collection on microfiche.

Ordering information: Full text of ERIC Documents (a subset of what is accessible via ERIC) are available by sending E-mail to edrs@gmuvm.gwu.edu, or via telephone to the Eric Document Reproduction Service, (800) 443-ERIC or (703) 440-1400.

ERIC accessibility at Syracuse University is sponsored by Syracuse University, not by ERIC. Continued free access is not guaranteed. The degree of long-term commitment to free provision of Internet access to ERIC at Auburn and Saskatchewan is not known.

Title: ERIC Digests
Resource Type: Database

ERIC produces about 150 new digests each year. These are literature reviews and summaries of a topical area, each produced by one of the sixteen ERIC Clearinghouses. The digests are excellent sources of citations to key works in the topic areas and offer quick handy summaries of the topic.

Authors: The sixteen ERIC clearinghouses
Author telephone number: 1-800-LET-ERIC

File name: `ERIC-digests.src` or `eric-digest.src` (WAIS source description files)
File formats: WAIS database
Data format: Text only
File size (for each format above): over 850 digests, each about 1,000 to 1,500 words each 7,000 printed pages total

Primary/authoritative source: `telnet sunsite.unc.edu`
Instructions for access:

1. Log on as `swais`
2. Choose `ERIC Digests`
3. Enter keywords, press return to start the search
4. One-line document citations are returned. Highlight them with the cursor keys and press return to see the full text.

Additional sources/methods: Any WAIS client may search this source directly (see Chapter 2). WAIS sources for this database exist at `sun-wais.oit.unc.edu` and `nic.sura.net`. Many Gopher servers offer access to this source as well.

Last known revision date: April 1992
Number of revisions to date: ERIC database updated quarterly since 1990. This WAIS database has not been updated.
First issue: 1992
Next planned revision/planned frequency of revision: Quarterly for 1993. Approximately 150 new digests per year are created; old digests remain available, via print or magnetic tape from ERIC.

Copyright restriction: None

Experience level: General
Target audience: Mostly academic. The ERIC Digests offer scholarly appraisals and summaries of timely topics, including citations to the most important published works in the area.
Environment applicability: This source is searchable through either WAIS or Gopher. The entire unformatted database is available directly from ERIC for a small cost.

Notes: See the pages on the ERIC Bibliographic Database for more details on the ERIC database.

Title: Geographic Name Server
Resource Type: Database

This resource consists of an interactive database that contains information on the city names, county names, population, latitude, longitude, zip codes, and other items for thousands of U.S. cities and some international locations. It accepts simple queries and provides the best matches. You can query on any of the available fields.

Author: Tim Libert
Author Affiliation/institution: University of Michigan
Author E-mail: libert@citi.umich.edu
Author USPS address: CITI/lfs, 519 Argus #4943, Ann Arbor, MI 26161.
Author telephone number: (313) 764-5548

File formats: Indexed
Number of files: Inaccessible to user
Data format: Field-formatted
File size: Unknown

Primary/authoritative source: `telnet martini.eecs.umich.edu 3000`
Instructions for access: No log-on name or password needed. Type `help` or `info` for assistance, `logoff` or `quit` to exit.
Additional sources/methods: Client software will be made available in the future.

Last known revision date: Unknown
Number of revisions to date: 1991
First issue: Unknown
Next planned revision/planned frequency of revision: Clients and enhanced searching capabilities are under development.

Copyright restriction: None.

Experience level: Searching is easy, but interpreting the output is not entirely straightforward.
Target audience: Anyone who wants to look up a geographic location by zip code, city name, longitude/latitude, or a number of other methods.
Environment applicability: Client software would make this easier to use and is under development. Currently, the only access method is via telnet, and the output is not formatted to be easily interpreted by humans.

Notes: Make sure to include the port number in your telnet command! If you are prompted for a username you are not connected correctly.

Title: Project Gutenberg
Resource Type: Electronic texts

Project Gutenberg is the original effort to create and distribute electronic versions of books (known as e-texts) free of charge. The holdings include items for a general audience (*Alice in Wonderland*), reference tools (*Roget's Thesaurus*), general computer and network guides, and classics (*Paradise Lost*), among other things.

Director: Michael Hart
Director Affiliation/institution: Project Gutenberg
Director E-mail: dircompg@ux1.cso.uiuc.edu
Director postal address: Illinois Benedictine College, Lisle, IL 60532
Telephone number: contact David Turner at (708) 960-1500

File format: Text
Number of files: more than forty-eight, as of March 1993
Data format: Text
File size: Varies from several hundred to many thousands of lines. Plain text and zipped versions of each e-text are available.

Primary/authoritative source: `ftp mrcnext.cso.uiuc.edu`
Instructions for access: `cd pub/e-text; ascii; get 0INDEX.GUT` (upper case) for index, or `cd` and `ls` to identify specific texts stored in subdirectory by year of release.
Additional sources/methods: Gutenberg texts are widely distributed on FTP and Gopher sites. Some texts are also distributed on CD-ROM products.

Last known revision date: March 1993
Number of revisions to date: More than twenty-eight
First issue: 1971. Only materials since 1991 are currently available.
Next planned revision/planned frequency of revision: New e-texts are added every month. The output doubles yearly. In 1993 there will be four new e-texts per month, in 1994 there will be eight. The Project is due to run through 2001, for a total of over 10,000 e-texts.

Copyright restriction: Texts may be copied and distributed freely. See the copyright notice at the top of each text for details.

Experience level: Most texts are for a general audience.
Target audience: Everyone
Environment applicability: The texts are in plain ASCII form and are accessible from any computer or program.

Content sample: (`from pub/e-text/e-text91/alice29.txt`)

CHAPTER I

Down the Rabbit-Hole

Alice was beginning to get very tired of sitting by her sister on the bank, and of having nothing to do: once or twice she had peeped into the book her sister was reading, but it had no pictures or conversations in it, 'and what is the use of a book,' thought Alice 'without pictures or conversation?'

Notes: "If you need a disk copy, please send a donation to: Project Gutenberg, Illinois Benedictine College, 5700 College Road, Lisle, IL 60532-0900. Be sure to include the exact type of disk you want. You can also subscribe to a paper edition of their electronic Newsletter at this address for an additional donation." (from the director)

Title: Weather Underground
Resource Type: Database

Weather is available from a number of places. The Weather Underground is one of the friendliest weather services and also one of the most complete. See `Help` for other sources of weather information.

Provider: College of Engineering
Provider affiliation/institution: University of Michigan
Provider E-mail: sdm@madlab.sprl.umich.edu
Provider postal address: Ann Arbor, MI 48109-2143

File format: Database
Number of files: Unknown
Data format: Various formatted text
File size: Unknown

Primary/authoritative source: `telnet downwind.sprl.umich.edu 3000`
Instructions for access: Follow menu instructions, `H` for help.
Additional sources/methods:

1. UIUC Gopher (`gopher gopher.uiuc.edu`).
2. `ftp vmd.cso.uiuc.edu; cd wx` for current GIF images

First issue: Unknown
Next planned revision/planned frequency of revision: Hourly

Copyright restriction: "The Weather Underground requests that you acknowledge the National Science Foundation, the UNIDATA project, and the University of Michigan as the supplier or the data if you are redistributing the data to a wide audience (potentially 100 users or more)." (from the `Help` option)

Target audience: General
Environment applicability: United States and Canada only

Content note:

WEATHER UNDERGROUND MAIN MENU
1) U.S. forecasts and climate data
2) Canadian forecasts
3) Current weather observations

4) Ski conditions
5) Long-range forecasts
6) Latest earthquake reports
7) Severe weather
8) Hurricane advisories
9) National Weather Summary
10) International data
11) Marine forecasts and observations
X) Exit program
C) Change scrolling to screen
H) Help and information for new users
?) Answers to all your questions

7
FTP Directories

Sometimes You Need to Browse

Across the Internet there are more than one thousand places where you can use Anonymous FTP to access data, software, and other resources. There is quite a bit of redundancy out there, but not as much as there used to be. Archie is the key tool for searching FTP sites for a particular item (see Chapter 2).

This chapter includes some of the key sites for Anonymous FTP. Some are key because they have everything, others are key because they are of interest to a particular user community, and a few are key because they have special collections that are not accessible elsewhere.

As you become familiar with FTP-able resources, two important characteristics of the available resources will become clear to you. The first characteristic is that you are likely to be able to find some sort of match for almost anything you are looking for, whether it is software or some sort of data. The collective work of years spent by Internet users to make their own environments somewhat better has resulted in a plethora of freely available software and other resources (this book only skims the cream from the vast quantity of what's out there). This is one of the wonderful things about computer networking: Individuals or groups who choose to make their work available may do so easily, to the benefit of all.

The second characteristic presents the problem: There are few indirect ways to assess the content, quality, authorship, or currency of items available via FTP. Good resources are redistributed. Some are updated. Others might have their filenames changed. One filename might refer to more than one resource. The original source of a resource might be unidentifiable. Add to these problems the tendancy for people and hosts to relocate or end up with different user/host names, and you are left with some real barriers to effective use of FTP.

To summarize: (1) something you want is out there and (2) the thing you want might be difficult to find. Hence browsing. You may find it necessary to use a combination of Archie with your knowledge of likely FTP sites for particular resources, plus iterative use of the FTP commands `ls`, `cd`, and `get`, in order to find what you are looking for (or to confirm its non-existence).

This chapter includes some of the best places to look for particular resources, but don't forget about the rest of the FTP sites mentioned in this book. The FTP sites in this chapter are generally the larger ones, yet individuals may make materials available via FTP to a site in which little else is available—once again, you need to rely on the community of your friends and peers to keep you informed of the wherabouts of particular resources of interest.

One final note: The FTP sites included in this chapter are not intended to be representative of all the "good" FTP sites on the Internet. The other chapters include many sites that are not replicated here. A large number of sites, usually at least one in every country active in Internet-ing, hold relatively complete collections of commonly used network resources and software. Be sure to check local sites before using international links to copy files with FTP.

FTP Etiquette

1. Supply your E-mail address as a password when requested. This is used by system administrators to track usage patterns and identify sources of trouble.

2. Most FTP sites should only be used during off-peak hours. This is typically from either 6:00 P.M. to 7:00 A.M. or 11:00 P.M. to 7:00 A.M. local time. Do not access FTP resources during peak hours unless the README file or log on message says it may be used during peak times.

3. FTP takes up network bandwidth. Generally, you should avoid transfer of large files during peak usage times because they will slow down users who are employing interactive resources. The file will still be there tonight, or early tomorrow morning.

4. Choose the closest site with the file you want. You should first look for a site in your domain (e.g., the .edu domain or the .uk domain). The larger academic and commercial sites tend to have the highest bandwidth connections. Larger means more users, more computers, and higher bandwidth connectivity with regional or national networks. Connect to these "high traffic" sites, if you have a choice, instead of smaller scale sites. The reason for this is that you can guess with some accuracy that the smaller sites will have a slower connection to the Internet—so, your file transfer will take longer, and you will employ a larger proportion of the remote site's network bandwidth.

5. Remember that FTP sites are provided voluntarily, and the system administrator may have little knowledge of the resources available on his or her site.

Title: ftp.eff.org
Resource Type: FTP Directory

The Electronic Frontier Foundation is an organization which is devoted to the protection of civil rights in Cyberspace. "We have defended civil liberties in court. We have shaped the policy debate on emerging communications infrastructure and regulation. We have increased awareness both on the Net and among those law enforcement officials, policy makers and corporations whose insufficient understanding of the digital environment threatened the freedom of Cyberspace. Yet there is still much to be done (from about-eff)."

Corporate author: The Electronic Frontier Foundation (EFF)
Corporate E-mail: eff@eff.org
Corporate postal address: Electronic Frontier Foundation, Inc., 666 Pennsylvania Avenue S.E., Suite 303, Washington, DC 20003
Corporate telephone number: (202) 544 9237

File format: Various
Number of files: Several hundred
Data format: Mostly text
File size: Mostly under 50KB

Primary/authoritative source: `ftp ftp.eff.org`

Copyright restriction: Most materials may be freely distributed

Experience level: Some materials assume familiarity with networking terminology and history.
Target audience: People interested in shaping and understanding the future of computer networking
Environment applicability: Most materials have to do with U.S. policy.

Notes: Individual and institutional membership in EFF is available.

A Gopher service is also available. Not all materials available via FTP are currently available by Gopher. The Gopher site is `gopher.eff.org`. This is a representative menu from the EFF Gopher server:

Electronic Frontier Foundation Files & Information

1. Search the EFF on-line document library <?>
2. Back issues of EFFector Online and EFF News/
3. Search the archives of comp.org.eff.talk <?>
4. Papers and testimony by EFF staff & board members/
5. EFF Newsnotes & FYI postings/
6. Treatises on Cyberspace and its denizens the Cyberpunks/
7. Discussion of various legal issues affecting the Net & denizens th../
8. Text of various laws and proposed laws relevant to the Electronic ../

Title: List of Anonymous FTP Sites with Content Summaries
Resource Type: List

When maintained, this list was the source of choice for information about where to find something via anonymous FTP. It has since been replaced by Archie. However, the list is still useful for at least two purposes. First, it is relatively small and can be searched rapidly for sites or resources for which you have a name or partial name. Second, it has IP addresses for the sites it indexes, which are sometimes hard to obtain otherwise. This list is out of date: beware of inaccurate information.

Author: Jon Granrose
Author E-mail: odin@pilot.njin.net

File format: Text

Data format: One-line summaries of FTP address & contents
File size: 148KB, 2,063 lines

Primary/authoritative source: `ftp pilot.njin.net`
Instructions for access: `cd pub/ftp-list; ascii; get ftp.list`
Additional sources: Some other FTP sites

Last known revision date: December 1991
Number of revisions to date: Was updated monthly
First issue: Unknown
Next planned revision/planned frequency of revision: None

Copyright restriction: unlimited redistribution

Target audience: FTP users
Environment applicability: This list points to software and data for all computing and networking environments.

Content sample:

zaphod.ncsa.uiuc.edu	141.142.20.50	mac X programs, ncsa telnet,
zaphod.ncsa.uiuc.edu		Heirarchical Data File
zaphod.ncsa.uiuc.edu		system, misc graphics &
zaphod.ncsa.uiuc.edu		scientific formats
zaphod.ncsa.uiuc.edu	08/13/90	anonymous/odin@pilot.njin.netz

Title: nnsc.nsf.net
Resource Type: FTP site

This is the main distribution site for NSFNET, which until recently was largely synonymous with "The Internet." Network policies, publications, and a collection of general networking information make this a key site for definitive information about networking.

Maintainer: The National Science Foundation
Maintainer E-mail: NSF Network Service Center <nnsc@nnsc.nsf.net>

Primary/authoritative source: `ftp nnsc.nsf.net`
Instructions for access: `get HELP` for general information
Additional sources/methods: A mail server is available for the same holdings. Send a message to `info-request@nnsc.nsf.net` with the following text to get started:

```
request: info
topic: help
```

Copyright restriction: Most resources are copyright free

Target audience: All network users.

Environment applicability: Most information applies to any TCP/IP-based network, some information applies to any sort of computer network.

Title: Online Book Initiative
Resource Type: FTP site

The Online Book Initiative (OBI) is a sizable collection of public-domain electronic texts. The texts include more than just standard books, including such items as press releases, word lists, and speeches. Items are organized by subdirectory.

Maintainer: Barry Shein
Host institution: The World (network service provider)
Maintainer E-mail: bzs@world.std.com

Number of files:
File format: Text and compressed text
File size: Varies from hundreds to millions of bytes.

Primary/authoritative source: ftp or gopher to world.std.com.
Environment applicability: Some texts are "plain," others are formatted with markup codes suitable for text processing software input.

Directory listing: (these are the names of the subdirectories available)

A.E.Housman, A.Hofmann, ACN, ATI, Access, Aesop, Ambrose.Bierce, Amoeba, Anarchist, Anonymous, Ansax, Antartica, ArtCom, Athene, BSD, BSDI, Bell.Labs, Bill.Gates, BookReviews, CCITT, CERT, CSNET, Census, Charles.Dickens, Charles.Hedrick, Charles.Lutwidge.Dodgson, Classics, Colin.Higgins, CompSci, Computer.U.Digest, Conspiracy, CounterRants, DARPA, DEC, DOD, DOS, DecWRL, Desert.Storm, Dictionary, Doyle, EC, ECPA, EFF, Economics, Edwin.Abbott, Emily.Bronte, Esperanto, Ethnologue, Ezra.Pound, FIPS, FSF, Fairy.Tales, FoundingFathers, GIFNews, GNU, George.Bush, Grimm, Gutenberg, H.H.Munro, HM.recipes, Haring, Harkin, Henry.David.Thoreau, HighTechReports, Hiroshima.Survivors, History, Holocaust, Hugo.Awards, Hypertext, IBM, Ingar.Holst, Internet, IrishEmigrant, J.W.Barrie, JFK, James.Allen, James.Matthew.Barrie, Jane.Austen, Jnl.Distance.Ed, John.Milton, Joseph.Conrad, Karl.Marx, Katherine.Mansfield, Kipling, LPF, Legal, Lewis.Carroll, Lysander.Spooner, Macintosh, Maps, Martin.Luther.King, Mathematica, Melville, Misc, Mischief, NIH, NIST, Nerd.Humor, NetSpellbook, NetWeaver, Networking, NewBooks, NewsLetters, OTA, OtherRealms, Patents, Paul.Tsongas, Percy.Bysshe.Shelley, Philip.Agee, Phone.Dirs, Phracks, Pointers, Police.Notes, Postmodern, PubWare, Quanta, Quotes, REACH, Rants, Recipes, Reed.de.Buch, Religion, Roget, SUG, Shakespeare, Soviet.Archives, Standards, Star.Trek.Parodies, Star.Trek.Stories, Stocks, Sun.Microsystems, Supreme.Court, TechReports, Tennyson, Thesis, Titles, Tracy.LaQuey, U.S.Congress, UFO, US.StateDept, USE-

NET, USENIX, USElection, USG, USPatents, Unix, Usenet.Cookbook, Usenix, VMS, Vatasyayana, Vatican, Walter.Scott, Weather.Maps, Wilfred.Owen, William.Blake, William.Butler.Yeats, William.Jefferson.Clinton, WordLists, World.Factbook, Xinu, Youngs.Science, ZIPCODES, crucible, desert-storm.irc.5, hakmem.order, marshall.islands, opinions.supreme-court, pr, tahiti

Title: seq1.loc.gov
Resource Type: FTP site

The Library of Congress is a relative latecomer to Internet-based information provision, but they have recently made an excellent collection of resource guides, bibliographies, and LOC information available. They currently provide two online art exhibits one of The Vatican and one of Soviet Archives. These exhibits consist of text files and GIF images relating to physical exhibits in the LOC. This site should be a first stop for almost any research project.

Institution: Library of Congress
Maintainer E-mail: Bob Zich <rzic@seq1.loc.gov>
Maintainer USPS address: Washington, DC 20540
Maintainer telephone number: (202) 707-6233

Number of files: > 175
Data format: Plain or formatted text
File size: From 1KB to over 400KB

Primary/authoritative source: `ftp seq1.loc.gov`
Instructions for access: Use `cd` `ls` and `get` to identify and retrieve files.
Additional sources/methods: None, but Gopher service is in progress.

Last known revision date: new materials are added each month
Copyright restriction: None

Experience level: Some materials require background knowledge to be useful.
Target audience: Many targeted audiences, especially for bibliographies and resource guides

Directories found under `/pub/Library.of.Congress`:

`about.LC/` Files describing services available from different areas within the Library of Congress.

`research.guides/` Files containing text of research guides such as finding aids and bibliographies produced by various divisions of the Library of Congress.

Title: wuarchive.wustl.edu
Resource Type: FTP site

WUARCHIVE is the most likely single place to have whatever you are looking for. It is also the most likely place to find yourself suffering from information overload. WU strives to provide access to all of the high-quality network resources in one place.

An important feature of this FTP site is that the subdirectories may be mounted across the Internet using NFS. NFS (for Network File System) is a method for making a remote computer's disk drive appear to be a part of your own local computer, so that files may be viewed, copied, and otherwise manipulated as though they were on your local machine. (NFS must be performed by a system administrator.)

Maintaining institution: Washington University, St. Louis
Environment applicability: Items in this site are without prejudice to computer hardware or software, although there is a tendency toward English language materials. Most items are software (as opposed to text files or other data).

Note: The listing of all files is in `pub/info/files.1st` (over 20MB!).

Some FTP Sites to Try

These sites are listed alphabetically by their sponsoring agency. The agency name constitutes the first word(s) in the descriptive text. Notice that these nodes may change names. If you get a "host unknown" message, or are denied access as an "`anonymous`" FTP user, try adding an "`ftp.`" to the front of the node, or substitute "`ftp.`" for the first part of the node name listed here.

ftp.ans.net

Advanced Networking Services (ANS) is one of the important forces involved in the transition of the Internet from a research community to a commercial enterprise. The `pub/info` subdirectory contains various documents which are helpful in understanding this process.

ftp.apple.com

Apple has brought together some of the popular public-domain software and shareware with their own bug fixes and a good collection of free software at this FTP site. As expected, most of the materials are suitable only for Apple computers running Apple or AUX operating systems.

research.att.com

AT&T (The American Telephone and Telegraph Company) maintains a site for distribution and archives of their research activities. This site includes research reports, archives, and software. These materials are available via standard anonymous FTP. You may also provide `netlib` as an FTP log-on name to access the NETLIB services (see page 96). AT&T is the producer of a number of libraries available via NETLIB.

chalmers.se

The Chalmers University of Technology maintains a representative collection of public domain network software. There is also a Gopher server at `gopher.chalmers.se` that contains many Swedish language materials as well as links to other Gopher servers.

cnam.cnam.fr

CNAM holds a good collection of software and papers about networking in both French and English. A Gopher server may be forthcoming at `gopher.cnam.fr`.

watsun.cc.columbia.edu

Columbia University is the origination point for Kermit software. Kermit is perhaps the best general purpose software for terminal emulation and file transfer, if only because it's both free and available for every popular computer system currently available. Restrictions on commercial uses make this less seldom seen in companies and on commercial networking systems than in academic environments and among local BBSs and networks.

gatekeeper.dec.com

DEC Research Corporation maintains this site. It contains a wide-ranging collection of both standard network resources and miscellany. A subdirectory called `recipes` contains hundreds of recipes to try. This is a also a depository for software for Ultrix and VMS (the operating systems found on DEC computers).

nic.ddn.mil

The Defense Data Network (U.S.) maintains an authoritative collection of protocols, Requests for Comments (RFCs), and other data about networking. This is also the site at which network routing information and registration services are kept.

ftp.funet.fi and gopher.funet.fi

The Finnish Academic and Research Network (FUNET) maintains this FTP site. It contains a good collection of general networking resources and software intended for use by the Finnish community. Most materials are available elsewhere. The Gopher server contains English and Finnish language material, and points to many other sites in Finland and the rest of Europe.

prep.ai.mit.edu

The Free Software Foundation produces GNU software. These are high-quality free software products that work on Unix and other computer system types. If all software were written as well as GNU, and with such a focus on continued updates and continued cross-platform compatibility, the world would be a safer place. Note that FSF recommends that you do NOT get GNU software directly from the MIT site. Instead, try one of these in your network neighborhood:

Asia: ftp.cs.titech.ac.jp, utsun.s.u-tokyo.ac.jp:/ftpsync/prep, cair.kaist.ac.kr:/pub/gnu
Australia: archie.oz.au:/gnu (archie.oz or archie.oz.au for ACSnet)
Europe: src.doc.ic.ac.uk:/gnu, ftp.informatik.tu-muenchen.de, ftp.informatik.rwth-aachen.de:/pub/gnu, nic.funet.fi:/pub/gnu, ugle.unit.no, isy.liu.se, ftp.stacken.kth.se, ftp.win.tue.nl, ftp.denet.dk, ftp.eunet.ch, nic.switch.ch:/mirror/gnu, irisa.irisa.fr:/pub/gnu, grasp1.univ-lyon1.fr:pub/gnu, archive.eu.net
United States: wuarchive.wustl.edu, ftp.cs.widener.edu, uxc.cso.uiuc.edu, col.hp.com:/mirrors/gnu, gatekeeper.dec.com:/pub/GNU, ftp.uu.net:/systems/gnu

ftp.lth.se and gopher.lth.se

The Lund Institute of Technology holds a good general collection of network software archives. These are most useful for those close to Sweden. The associated Gopher server at `gopher.lth.se` is a gateway to several Swedish Gopher sites.

athena-dist.mit.edu

The Massachusetts Institute of Technology supports Project Athena. Among other things, this is the distribution point for Kerberos, a user-to-host security system for Internet hosts.

ftp.merit.edu

Merit, Inc. is a principle player in the day-to-day operation of the United States portions of the Internet. Of key interest at this site is the `statistics` subdirectory, which contains traffic statistics for NSFNET from 1991 to the present. This is where the widely-cited statistics on the growth of the Internet originate. (Another FTP site is `merit.edu,` which has some overlap with the contents of `ftp.merit.edu`).

Listing of subdirectories:

    acceptable.use.policies
    bin
    cise
    documents
    etc
    internet
    introducing.the.internet
    lib
    maps
    merit
    michnet

      newsletters
      nren
      nsfnet
      omb
      resources
      statistics
      usr
      working.groups

ftp.msen.com (also gopher.msen.com)

MSEN, an Internet service provider includes *Internet Business Pages,* a yellow pages service for network-related enterprises and *The Internet Review,* a casual journal about network resources. A Gopher service is available via `gopher.msen.com`. The Gopher contains lots of good resources. Edward Vielmetti <emv@msen.com> is the maintainer of the data and also the vice-president of MSEN. He is active in the maintenance and provision of several WAIS databases.

nptn.org

The National Public Telecomputing Network (NPTN) is the moving force behind the Free-Net movement. Consult this FTP site for current listings of available Free-Net sites. See the directory `pub/info.nptn` for the Blue Book, which explains the process of starting your own community Free-Net.

black.ox.ac.uk

The Oxford Text Archive make this an interesting site. It contains information on the many texts available in electronic form (unfortunately, most of these are NOT in the public domain and require formal agreements with the OTA). See the file `black.ox.ac.uk:pub/ota/textarchive.info` for details. The wordlists directory is also a good attraction, containing numerous lists of words in various languages.

sumex-aim.stanford.edu

Stanford University holds one of the best collections of software for Apple computers. See the `info-mac` subdirectory for subdirectory names including: app, art, card, comm, cp, da, demo, digest, ex, fkey, font, game, help, lang, misc, report, sound, source, tech, tips, unix, util, virus.

ftp.nisc.sri.com

SRI International is the producer of the list of mailing lists (see Chapter 5). SRI International also keeps archives of RFCs and drafts of standards produced by the Internet Engineering Task Force (IETF). The RFCs and IETF drafts serve as the operating rules for the Internet.

Contents (from the README file):

rfc and fyi	All the online RFCs and FYIs
ien	Internet Engineering Notes
iesg	Minutes from the IETF Steering Group
ietf	Minutes from IETF working groups
netinfo	General informational files on the Internet
internet-drafts	Drafts on standards from the IETF working groups
pub	General information
bboard-archives	Archives for tcp-ip, namedroppers and cisco

ftp.edu.tw

The National Chiao Tung University, Hsinchu, Taiwan, stores programs of interest to residents of Taiwan and China, including some software for enabling Chinese characters to be displayed on a PC.

wsmr-simtel20.army.mil

The United States Army, at the White Sands Missile Range, maintains a rarity among FTP sites: a collection of software for a wide range of computer types, including VMS, Unix, Macintosh, PC, and even CPM. There is also a collection of Ada code and utilities. This is a TOPS20 system, so the first file you should probably retrieve is `HOW-TO-CD.DOC`. This collection is mirrored elsewhere, including at `oak.oakland.edu`.

uxc.cso.uiuc.edu

The University of Illinois at Urbana-Champaign maintains several FTP servers of interest, of which UXC is the principal. Others are `ux1.cso.uiuc.edu`, `a.cs.uiuc.edu`, and `ftp.ncsa.uiuc.edu`. Among these sites may be found a high-quality cross-section of resources available across the Internet, as well as a number of resources developed by the various units at UIUC. On UXC the `Netinfo` subdirectory is of particular interest.

utsun.s.u-tokyo.ac

The University of Tokyo maintains this central site for the University of Tokyo International Science Network (TISN). It contains a large archive of Japanese freeware and general networking software.

vacs.uwp.edu

The University of Wisconsin at Parkside offers Gopher and FTP services. Of particular interest is the `music` subdirectory/menu item. Here you will find the lyrics of thousands of songs, as well as other information about the music world.

Music subdirectories include the following:

Artists- Archives by Artist name
Classical Buying Guide
Music Database program
Discographies
Frequently Asked Questions files
Folk Music Files and pointers
Guitar TAB files from ftp.nevada.edu
rec.music.info newsgroup archives
Interviews with musicians/groups
Kurzweil K2000 Archives
Mailing lists archives
Lyrics Archives
Some midi files
Misc files that don't fit anywhere else
GIFS, JPEGs, PBMs and more.
Press Releases and misc articles
Misc music-related programs for various machines
USA release listings (now info/releases)
rec.music.reviews archives
Short sound samples
Usenet Artist Polls

ftp.uu.net

UUNET is a central gateway for UUNET to Internet traffic. It also holds one of the largest general purpose FTP collections. Newsgroup archives, software, and many other things may be found here.

borg.lib.vt.edu

Virginia Polytechnic Institute and State University and University Libraries keep Scholarly Communication electronic journal archives. These currently include the following:

The Community Services CATALYST
Journal of Fluids Engineering (Raw Research Data)
Journal of Technology Education
Journal of the International Association of Hospitality Research
Modal Analysis (Abstracts and Page Images)
VPIEJ-L Discussion List Archives

8
Special Interest and Regional Resources

Joining an Internet Community

Communities are the foundation of the Internet. Without the people who make up Internet communities, there really wouldn't be any point—the mere existence of a telecommunications infrastructure does not mean that there is anything to do, or anyone to talk to.

This chapter is to help you to get in touch with an Internet community you share interests with. There are many such communities—every mailing list has its own small (or large) member group that exchanges messages. Larger communities share interests and collectively subscribe to some of the same mailing lists and newsgroups and use the same resources. These may be people you see at professional meetings, people with the same college major as you, or people who have similar hobbies or interests.

One of the greatest things the Internet does is to allow you to become a community member without sharing more than a narrow range of interests with the other community members. What does this mean? Consider what happens in the noncomputerized world: People you are most likely to run into, or socialize with, or exchange messages with, are those with whom you share similar global interests and backgrounds. So if you are a librarian, who has an interest in electric trains as a hobby, then you are most likely (and its easier) to interact with other librarians or train hobbyists.

But what if you realize you would like to find out more about baseball, or dog grooming, or antique cars? With a computer, you only need to subscribe to a mailing list or two, search through the archives of a Usenet group, and maybe complete an Archie search, and you have crossed the threshold to another community far more quickly than you could without the network. This beats buying a specialty magazine, because magazines don't talk back and answer questions (at least not quickly). It also beats going to your local club of, say, antique auto enthusiasts, because you can first listen in via the Internet to get comfortable with the language and topics under discussion before you join in on a conversation—and no one even needs to know you were there. For most of us, this is a far less imposing way to start getting involved with a group.

What this boils down to is some spectacular abilities that are facilitated by the Internet: The ability to belong to several communities that otherwise have little overlap, to listen in on discussions among community members you might like to join, and to engage others in conversation on a common topic regardless of what other interests you do not share. This is a way to bring the world closer together, at least a little at a time. Because communication is the method by which we learn and share our values, global communication and community boundary sharing can go a long way toward increasing understanding among diverse groups.

The other side of community building may be seen implicitly in the number and variety of mailing lists and newsgroups: Internet communities can exist on a state, national, or global scale, even if there are insufficient numbers locally for any substantial sharing. You can engage in conversation with hundreds of people worldwide who have an interest you share—perhaps a hobby or perhaps a narrow professional area—rather than being alone or one of a few that you have access to locally, or who you might otherwise contact via telephone or letter.

Enjoy your non-networked communities. But open yourself up to a wider world of people who share your interests and are accessible via computer network.

Search Techniques

This chapter includes resources that are created by community members to help others identify resources of interest to them. However, it is not the only way to get in touch with the right mailing list, newsgroup, or other resource. The lists of mailing lists and newsgroups in Chapter 5, in particular, are a good place to start. Use the searching capabilities of your computer or word processor to look for forums where topics you are interested in are being discussed. The chances are excellent that there will already be a community discussing your interests—all you need to do is join them.

Title: BIONET
Resource Type: Usenet hierarchy

BIONET is a collection of newsgroups devoted to various aspects of the biological sciences. An associated FTP site maintains archives, and the newsgroups are available via email to those without Usenet access.

File format: Text
Number of newsgroups: Several dozen, not all of which are active
Data format: Usenet articles

Primary/authoritative source: Usenet newsgroups in the bionet. hierarchy
Additional sources/methods:

1. FTP to turbo.bio.net; cd BIOSCI for archive directories.
2. Retrieve the file turbo.bio.net:doc/BIOSCI_info.sheet for information about receiving the individual newsgroups via email.

Last known revision date: Items are added to the archives as they are posted to the newsgroups.
First issue: Varies with newsgroup. Note that some newsgroups are defunct yet still archived.
Next planned revision/planned frequency of revision: Daily

Copyright restriction: Copyright remains with the originator of individual messages.

Target audience: Biological scientists, students, and others interested in biology.

Content summary (from `turbo.bio.net:doc/BIOSCI_info.sheet`):

List of BIOSCI Newsgroups

NEWSGROUP NAME	*TOPIC*
AGEING	Discussions about ageing research
AGROFORESTRY	Discussions about agroforestry research
ARABIDOPSIS	Newsgroup for the Arabidopsis Genome Project
BIOFORUM	Discussions about biological topics for which there is not yet a dedicated newsgroup
BIOLOGICAL-INFORMATION-THEORY-AND-CHOWDER-SOCIETY	Applications of information theory to biology
BIONAUTS	Question/answer forum for help using electronic networks, locating e-mail addresses, etc.
BIONEWS **	General announcements of widespread interest to biologists
BIO-JOURNALS	Tables of contents of biological journals
BIO-MATRIX	Applications of computers to biological databases
BIO-SOFTWARE	Information on software for the biological sciences
CHROMOSOME-22	Mapping and sequencing of human chromosome 22
COMPUTATIONAL-BIOLOGY **	Mathematical and computer applications in biology
EMBL-DATABANK	Messages to and from the EMBL database staff
EMPLOYMENT	Job opportunities
GDB	Messages to and from the Genome Data Bank staff
GENBANK-BB	Messages to and from the GenBank database staff
GENETIC-LINKAGE	Newsgroup for genetic linkage analysis
HIV-MOLECULAR-BIOLOGY	Discussions about the molecular biology of HIV
HUMAN-GENOME-PROGRAM	NIH-sponsored newsgroup on human genome issues
IMMUNOLOGY	Discussions about research in immunology
METHODS-AND-REAGENTS	Requests for information and lab reagents
MOLECULAR-EVOLUTION	Discussions about research in molecular evolution
NEUROSCIENCE	Discussions about research in the neurosciences
PLANT-BIOLOGY	Discussions about research in plant biology
POPULATION-BIOLOGY	Discussions about research in population biology
PROTEIN-ANALYSIS	Discussions about research on proteins and messages for the PIR and SWISS-PROT databank staffs

PROTEIN-CRYSTALLOGRAPHY   Discussion about crystallography of macromole-
                           cules and messages for the PDB staff
SCIENCE-RESOURCES   Information from/about scientific funding agencies
TROPICAL-BIOLOGY   Discussions about research in tropical biology
WOMEN-IN-BIOLOGY   Discussions about issues concerning women biolo-
                           gists

Note: The FTP site also holds software for using Gene Bank data.

Title: CCNEWS Events Calendar
Resource Type: Calendar

CCNEWS, published by EDUCOM, is an electronic service for campus computing newsletter editors. The CCNEWS Events Calendar is an up-to-date listing of conferences, semi-
nars, workshops, and other events related to information technology in higher education.

Corporate compiler: EDUCOM
Author E-mail: ccnews@bitnic.educom.edu

File format: Text
Number of files: One
Data format: Text
File size: 9KB, 320 lines

Primary/authoritative source: `listserv@bitnic.educom.edu`
Instructions for access: Send this text: `get events calendar ccnews`

Last known revision date: February 1993
Number of revisions to date: Unknown
First issue: 1989
Next planned revision/planned frequency of revision: Monthly

Copyright restriction: None

Target audience: Primarily people involved with higher education and campus computing
Environment applicability: The events in the file are the type that you need to attend in person—they are not network-based.

Sample entry:

  Computers in Libraries International '93
    DATE: Feb.23-25 1993
    CITY: London, UK
    CONTACT: 800-635-5537 or Meckler@jvnc.net

Title: COMSERVE
Resource Type: Mail and File Server

COMSERVE was started in 1986 and is an electronic disciplinary center for communication scholars, students, and other interested in human communication studies and related fields (telecommunications, rhetoric, speech, mass communications, social linguistics, etc.). It has a similar function and syntax to LISTSERV software. However, COMSERVE runs only at one location and provides many types of services not available with LISTSERV. COMSERVE maintains and archives about two dozen public mailing lists (called "hotlines") relating to communication. There is also a large collection of other materials relating to communication, including bibliographies, course syllabi, and so forth. Other important services include the maintenance of an up-to-date searchable index to print journals in communication and an electronic white pages for individuals in the field of communication. COMSERVE also is the site of publication of *The Electronic Journal of Communication / La Revue Electronique de Counication,* a bilingual peer-reviewed scholarly journal. In addition, COMSERVE can quiz you about your knowledge of human communication and can interact with users in English, Spanish, and Portuguese.

Corporate author: Communication Institute for Online Scholarship, Inc.
Author affiliation/institution: Rensselaer Polytechnic Institute
Author E-mail: Support@Vm.Its.Rpi.Edu
Author USPS address: P.O. Box 57, Rotterdam Junction, NY 12150 USA
Author phone number: (518) 887-2443

File format: Text
Number of files: Many hundreds
Data format: Plain or formatted text. Some CMS and VMS source code
File size: Varies. The total holdings include many Megabytes.

Primary/authoritative source: email to `comserve@vm.its.rpi.edu`
Instructions for access: Various COMSERVE commands. Try `help` first
Additional sources/methods: None

First issue: 1986
Next planned revision/planned frequency of revision: new items are added frequently. Archives of hotlines are supplemented daily.

Copyright restriction: Copyright (c) 1991 by the Communication Institute for Online Scholarship, Inc., P.O. Box 57, Rotterdam Junction, NY, 12150 USA. All rights reserved. Public or commercial use is prohibited (from output of "help" command sent to `comserve@vm.its.rpi.edu`).

Target audience: mostly communication scholars, but many materials apply to a wider audience. There is also a collection of materials relating to human-computer interaction and computer networking.

Sample output: (from `send comserve helpfile` command output)

Comserve is an electronic information service for people interested in human communication studies. This file provides a brief summary of Comserve's functions and its commands. This presentation is meant only as a summary. More options exist for many of the commands. For a finer level of detail, use Comserve's 'Help Topics' system and see the notes near the bottom of this document for information about how to obtain a copy of Comserve User's Guide.

Notes: BITNET users may interact with COMSERVE using line messaging. To facilitate this, VMS (`easycom.com`) and CMS (`easycom exec`) programs are available from COMSERVE.

Title: An Educator's Guide to E-Mail Lists
Resource Type: List

Two files are maintained as part of the EDNET mailing list archive. The first lists LIST-SERV mailing lists of interest to educators. The second list contains Usenet newsgroups.

Maintainer: Prescott Smith
Maintainer affiliation/institution: University of Massachusetts, Amherst
Maintainer E-mail: pgsmith@educ.umass.edu
Maintainer postal address: 160 Rolling Green, Amherst, MA 01002
Maintainer telephone number: (413) 253-5527

File format: Text
Number of files: Two
Data format: List
File size: 97KB, 1703 lines (`educatrs.lst`); 46KB, 872 lines (`edusenet.gde`)

Primary/authoritative source: `ftp nic.umass.edu`
Instructions for access: `cd pub/ednet; ascii; get edusenet.gde` (newsgroups); `get educatrs.lst` (mailing lists)
Additional sources/methods: Posted occasionally to the EDNET mailing list

Last known revision date: February 1993
Number of revisions to date: Unknown
First issue: Unknown
Next planned revision/planned frequency of revision: Unknown

Copyright restriction: None

Target audience: education professionals

Content summary: This is the organization scheme used for each file. From `README`.

Ed.
- Adult
- Higher, Academic
- Higher, Administrative
- Higher, Student
- Instructional Media
- International Related
- K12
- Multicultural Related
- Special

Arts

Computer

Computer

Software

Statistics

Women's Studies

Future Studies

Help

History & Humanities

Language - Communication Studies
- International
- Linguistics
- Literature
- Writing

Library & Information Retrieval

Philosophy

Science
- PC Biblio, Text
- Social

Note: To subscribe to the EDNET mailing list send this message to `list-serv@nic.umass.edu`: `subscribe ednet Your Name` (where `Your Name` is your real name, not your e-mail address).

Title: The Electric Mystic's Guide
Resource Type: Resource guide

"The Electric Mystic's Guide is a non-technical survey of all major documents, archives and services of relevance to Religious Studies and related fields that are available through the international, academic computer networks commonly referred to as the Net (BITNET, Internet, and affiliated networks). This includes networked papers, reviews, book notes, dissertations, major sacred texts, software programs, electronic mail address collections, general information files, data banks, electronic journals, newsletters, online discussion groups, specialized commercial and public networks, and relevant networked organizations, associations, institutions and companies (from the Introduction to Volume 1)."

Author: Michael Strangelove
Author affiliation/institution: University of Ottawa
Author E-mail: 441495@acadvm1.uottawa.ca
Author postal address: Religious Studies Department, 177 Waller, Ottawa, Ontario, K1N 6N5, Canada
Author telephone number: (613) 747-0642

File format: Text, PostScript, or WordPerfect
Number of files: One per volume (but split into multiple files for PostScript)
Number of volumes: Two
Data format: Plain and formatted text, plus indexes
File size: From 240K (text version) to over 2MB (PostScript version) per volume
ISSN: 1188-5734

Primary/authoritative source: `ftp panda1.uottawa.ca` (137.122.6.16)
Instructions for access: `cd pub/religion; get` various files depending on which
version you want. Filenames begin with `electric-mystics-guide`
Additional sources/methods: Also available via E-mail to `list-serv@acadvm1.uottawa.ca` with the commands `get mystics v1-txt` and `get mystics v2-txt` (plain text version only)

Last known revision date: February 1993
Number of revisions to date: Two major, many minor
First issue: 1992
Next planned revision/planned frequency of revision: Annually

Copyright restriction (from the text of Volume 1): Copyright (C) 1993 by Michael Strange-love. All Rights Reserved. This guide is intended for free dissemination as long as this header remains intact. Permission is hereby granted for noncommercial use by electronic bulletin board/conference systems, free-nets, individuals, and libraries. All commercial use requires the permission of the author. Scholar's Press is the only authorized distributor of print copies of this guide.
Target audience: of interest primarily to religion scholars

Content sample:

*   ANTHAP-L Archives

A fast growing collection of high-quality material from the Applied Anthropology Computer Network serving members of the Society for Applied Anthropology and the National Association for the Practice of Anthropology.

> Location: vela.acs.oakland.edu
>
> Directory: /pub/anthap/
>
> Contact: James Dow
>   Department of Sociology and Anthropology
>   dow@vela.acs.oakland.edu

Title: HCI Bibliography
Resource Type: Bibliography

"The HCI Bibliography is a free-access online extended bibliography on Human-Computer Interaction. The basic goal of the project is to put an online bibliography for most of HCI on the screens of all researchers, developers, educators and students in the field through anonymous ftp access, mail servers, and Mac and DOS floppy disks. Through the efforts of volunteers, the bibliography has reached 7000 entries" (from README).

Editor: Gary Perlman

Editor affiliation/institution: The Ohio State University
Editor E-mail: perlman@cis.ohio-state.edu
Editor USPS address: Department of Computer and Information Science, The Ohio State University, Columbus, OH 43210
Editor telephone number: (614) 292-2566

File format: Text
Number of files: 207
Data format: Fielded text using field identifiers from the Unix `refer` program
File size: Individual files range from several KB to several hundred KB. The entire collection exceeds 8.1MB

Primary/authoritative source: `ftp archive.cis.ohio-state.edu` (128.146.8.52)
Instructions for access: `cd pub/hcibib; ascii; get README` for detailed instructions.
Additional sources/methods: None

Last known revision date: March 1993
Number of revisions to date: Hundreds
First issue: 1989
Next planned revision/planned frequency of revision: At least quarterly

Copyright restriction: Many items are copyrighted. See the files `README` and `publish.txt` and the individual entries for details.

Target audience: Scholars and researchers in all aspects of human computer interaction.
Environment applicability: Although the refer program is used to format the data, they are easily readable by humans and may be processed into other forms.

Sample entry:

%T The Decoupled Simulation Model for Virtual Reality Systems
%S Tools & Architectures for Virtual Reality and Multi-User, Shared Data
%A Chris Shaw
%A Jiandong Liang
%A Mark Green
%A Yunqi Sun
%B Proceedings of ACM CHI'92 Conference on Human Factors in Computing Systems
%D 1992
%P 321-328
%K User interface software, Virtual reality, Interactive 3D graphics
%* (c) Copyright 1992 Association for Computing Machinery
%X The Virtual Reality user interface style allows the user to manipulate
(remainder of abstract deleted)

Content note: These are the current contents (from the editor)

Table 1: Books in the HCI Bibliography

Baecker & Buxton's	"Readings in HCI", Morgan-Kaufmann	1987
Galer et al	User-Centred Design for Info. Tech." Elsevier	1992
Helander's	"Handbook of HCI" Elsevier/North-Holland	1988
Salvendy's	"Handbook of Human Factors" Wiley	1987
Taylor et al	"Structure of Multimodal Dialogue" Elsevier	1992
van der Veer et al	"Cognitive Ergonomics" Elsevier	1989

Table 2: Conference Proceedings in the HCI Bibliography

BCS-HCI	People and Computers, Cambridge	1985-92
CHI	Human Factors in Computing Systems, ACM	1982-92
CQL	Computers and the Quality of Life, ACM	1990
CSCW	Computer-Supported Cooperative Work, ACM	1988, 90, 92
DPS	Document Processing Systems, ACM	1988
DOC	International Conference on Systems Documentation, ACM	1985, 88-92
ECHT	European Conference on Hypertext, Cambridge, ACM	1990
EP	Electronic Publishing, Cambridge	1990
ESP	Empirical Studies of Programmers, Ablex	1986, 87, 91
EWHCI	East-West International HCI, ICSTI	1992
HFS	Human Factors Society Annual Meeting, HFS	1987-91
HYPER	Hypertext Conference, ACM	1987, 89, 91
HYPUK	Hypertext I and II, Intellect	1988, 89
HYSTAN	Hypertext Standardization Workshop, NIST	1990
INT	IFIP INTERACT HCI Conference, Elsevier/North-Holland	1984, 87, 90
IR	Information Retrieval, ACM	1986-92
IWIUI	International Workshop on Intelligent User Interfaces, ACM	1993
MOSHCI	Moscow International HCI, ICSTI	1991
OCS	Organizational Computing Systems, ACM	1991
OIS	Office Automation/Information Systems, ACM	1982, 84, 86, 88, 90
UIST	User Interface Software and Technology, ACM	1986, 88-92

Table 3: Journal Volumes in the HCI Bibliography

BIT	Behaviour & Info. Tech., Taylor & Francis	v. 1-11; 1982-92
HCI	Human-Computer Interaction, Erlbaum	v. 1- 7; 1985-92
IESW	IEEE Software, IEEE	v. 4- 9; 1987-92
IJHCI	Intl. Jl. of Human-Computer Interaction, Ablex	v. 1- 4; 1989-92
IJMMS	Intl. Jl. of Man-Machine Studies, Academic Press	v. 1-37; 1969-92
IWC	Interacting with Computers, Butterworth-Heinemann	v. 1- 3; 1989-91
JOC	Jl. of Organizational Computing, Ablex	v. 1- 2; 1991-92
SIGCHI	Bulletin, ACM	v. 19-24; 1988-92
TOG	Transactions on Graphics, ACM	v. 5-11; 1986-92
TOIS	Transactions on (Office) Information Systems, ACM	v. 1-10; 1982-92

Title: Internet-Course at Pilot.njin.net
Resource Type: FTP site

This is a fairly small but rich source for files, software, and course materials for several courses concerning the Internet. Materials include tutorials/descriptions for FTP, emacs, and a list of "must have" resources for using the Internet. Some software is also included.

Authors: Various
Maintainer: Lou Bona
Maintainer E-mail: bona@pilot.njin.net

File formats: Mostly text, some software
Number of files: Thirty-one
Data format: Mostly text
File size (for each format above): Length of text files ranges from 53 lines (2,130 bytes) to 4883 lines (230KB). Software items from 200-500KB.

Primary/authoritative source: `ftp pilot.njin.net`
Instructions for access: `cd pub/Internet-course;` use `ls` to view available files.
Additional sources/methods: Individual components may be available from the authors or through alternate FTP sites.

Last known revision date: February 1993
Number of revisions to date: new items are added periodically, some items are updated.
First issue: earliest item is from 1991
Next planned revision/planned frequency of revision: None planned, but new resources may be added.

Copyright restriction: May be freely distributed or modified, provided credit is given to the authors.

Experience level: Directed at the novice, but useful for all network users.
Target audience: The courses were directed at K-12 educators, but have general applicability.
Environment applicability: Assumes Internet connectivity, with a preference for Unix

Title: Law Resources
Resource Type: List

Mailing lists, newsgroups, FTP sites, and law libraries on the Internet. Resources that pertain to law librarianship, law practice, legal education, and so forth. Listed are 180 mailing lists, 27 law libraries, a couple of FTP sites, and over 100 newsgroups.

Author: Mary Jensen
Author affiliation/institution: School of Law, University of South Dakota
Author E-mail: mjensen@charlie.usd.edu

Author postal address: 414 E. Clark St., Vermillion, SD 57069-2390
Author telephone number: (605) 677-6363

File format: Text
Number of files: One
Data format: List
File size: 47KB, 1184 lines

Primary/authoritative source: `ftp liberty.uc.wlu.edu`
Instructions for access: `cd pub/lawlib; get intresources.law`
Additional sources/methods: None

Last known revision date: August 1992
Number of revisions to date: None
Next planned revision/planned frequency of revision: None

Copyright restriction: Can't be reproduced commercially. Can be reproduced and distributed for no more than the actual cost of copying and distribution. Contains substantial amounts of material from other bibliographies which may have their own copyright restrictions (from the author).

Target audience: Law librarians

Content sample:

    LB: Columbia University Law Library
    TA: pegasus.law.columbia.edu
    TS: Innopac
    LI: At the login prompt, enter pegasus
    EX: Select J on the main menu.
    GU: Barron

Note: This bibliography is derived from a number of other Internet sources and is not a completely original work (from the author).

Title: Library-Oriented Mailing Lists
Resource Type: List

Librarians and other information professionals can use this resource to identify mailing lists and other resources of interest to them.

Author: Charles W. Bailey, Jr.
Author affiliation/institution: University of Houston
Author E-mail: Lib3@uhupvm1.uh.ed
Author postal address: University Libraries, University of Houston, Houston, TX 77204-2091
Author telephone number: (713) 743-9804

File format: Text
Number of files: Two
Data format: List
File size: 15KB, 356 lines

Primary/authoritative source: `Listserv@uhupvm1.uh.edu`
Instructions for access: Send email message `get library lists`
Additional sources/methods: None

Last known revision date: December 1992
Number of revisions to date: Unknown
First issue: Unknown
Next planned revision/planned frequency of revision: As new materials become available

Copyright restriction: Copyright (C) 1992 by Charles W. Bailey, Jr. All Rights Reserved. Copying is permitted for non-commercial use by academic computer centers, computer conferences, individual scholars, and libraries. This message must appear on all copied material. All commercial use requires permission (from the text).

Target audience: Librarians and information professionals

Content sample:

ADVANC-L@IDBSU	Geac Advance Library System
AFAS-L@KENTVM	African American Studies and Librarianship
ALF-L@YORKVM1	Academic Librarian's Forum
ARCHIVES@INDYCMS	Archives and Archivists List
ARIE-L@IDBSU	RLG Ariel Document Transmission System
ARLIS-L@UKCC	Art Libraries Association of North America
ASIS-L@UVMVM	American Society for Information Science
ATLAS-L@TCUBVM	Data Research ATLAS Users
AUTOCAT@UVMVM	Library Cataloging and Authorities Discussion Group

Title: LIBSOFT Archive
Resource Type: FTP site

The LIBSOFT Archive is a super resource for information professionals. It offers one-stop shopping for current versions of most (but not all) of the software and data used to access library resources. It also includes items to help educate information professionals about Internet.

Maintainer: Gord Nickerson
Maintainer affiliation/institution: University of Western Ontario
Maintainer E-mail: gnickers@uwo.ca
Maintainer telephone number: (519) 661-2199

File formats: Some text, some program
Number of files: 193
Data format: Varies
File size: Total archive is about 15MB. Individual files range from 1KB to over 600KB.

Primary/authoritative source: `ftp hydra.uwo.ca`
Instructions for access: `cd libsoft`; use `ls`, `cd` and `get` to identify and retrieve files.
`INDEX.TXT` contains a listing of currently available files.
Additional sources/methods: Most items in this archive are available elsewhere via FTP. No other site has the entire collection.

Last known revision date: March 1993
Number of revisions to date: Unknown
First issue: Unknown
Next planned revision/planned frequency of revision: As new items become available, usually monthly

Copyright restriction: Found in the individual items

Experience level: Varies
Target audience: Librarians, librarianship educators, other information professionals
Environment applicability: Some software will only run in a particular operating system environment.

Extract from a message from the maintainer:

"LIBSOFT contains programs of interest to librarians. File descriptions are in the file INDEX.TXT which you should read before transferring files. This site does not contain any general software (word processors, databases, etc.) as they are easily obtainable from the archives at simtel or its mirrors such as wuarchive.wustl.edu. LIBSOFT also has files to help librarians make use of the Internet."

Notes: This FTP host is a DEC computer running the VMS operating system. The most notable difference is that `cd ..` will not work to return to a higher directory level. Instead, use `cd [-]`

Title: Mailbase
Resource Type: Mail and File Server

Mailbase is a key locus for discussion groups pertaining to all aspects of scholarship related to the United Kingdom and Europe. "The Newcastle-based National Mailbase Service aims to support collaborative work amongst geographically distributed groups of researchers and associated support staff from within the U.K. higher education and research community. It does this by providing facilities for enhanced mailing lists and for information-sharing. Mailbase is freely available to such groups as a value-added networked service across JANET" (from `pub/mailbase/policy`).

Maintainer E-mail: nisp-team@mailbase.ac.uk or mailbase-helpline@mailbase.ac.uk
Service affiliation/institution: University of Newcastle Upon Tyne
Service postal address: The University of Newcastle Upon Tyne, Newcastle Upon Tyne, NE1 7RU, United Kingdom
Service telephone number: +44-91-222-6000

File format: Mostly text
Number of files: Several thousand
Data format: Mostly mailing list archives
Primary/authoritative source: E-mail to mailbase@mailbase.ac.uk
Instructions for access: Send E-mail to `mailbase@mailbase.ac.uk`. `help` is a good first command to send. The user guide may be retrieved with the command `send mailbase user-guide`
Additional sources/methods:

1. `Gopher` or anonymous FTP to `mailbase.ac.uk`
2. `telnet mailbase.ac.uk`, `login` as `guest`, `password` is `mailbase`. This is an interactive interface to the mailbase contents.

Copyright restriction: Copyright resides with the authors or the University of Newcastle. Most materials may be freely distributed but may not be sold.

Target audience: Primarily researchers in the United Kingdom and the rest of Europe

Notes: "Funding for the National Mailbase Service is provided by the UK's Information Systems Committee of the University Funding Council. The main criterion for establishing a new list is, therefore, that the list should benefit the UK higher education and research community. It is believed that this criterion is met if the list owner is UK-based and if there is a reasonable number of UK members on the list. It is clearly advantageous for the UK community to be able to share information with colleagues elsewhere" (From `/pub/ mailbase/policy`).

Title: Mother of All Eastern European Lists
Resource Type: List

This list includes mailing lists, newsgroups, databases, Gopher sites, and FTP sites of general interest to people who are from Eastern Europe or who have an interest in Eastern Europe. A number of the materials are in the language of the country under discussion.

Author: Zbigniew J. Pasek
Author affiliation/institution: University of Michigan
Author E-mail: zbigniew@engin.umich.edu
Author postal address: Department of Engineering, University of Michigan, Ann Arbor, MI 48109-2125
Author telephone number: (313) 747-4297

File format: Text
Number of files: One
Data format: List
File size: 35KB, 863 lines

Primary/authoritative source: `ftp piniecki.berkeley.edu`
Instructions for access: `cd pub/polish/network; ascii; get EE-MotherList`
Additional sources/methods: `gopher poniecki.berkeley.edu`
Last known revision date: December 1992
Number of revisions to date: Four major
First issue: June 1991
Next planned revision/planned frequency of revision: June 1993

Cost: Free
Copyright restriction: None

Experience level: Some resources require foreign language skills

Sample entry:

CONCISE is the COSINE Network's Central Information Service for Europe. CONCISE provides information about COSINE projects, networks, conferences, networking products, special interest groups, project databases, directories, Email services and other networked services in Europe. Available by e-mail, ftp and gopher.

> To obtain a copy of User guide on CONCISE send e-mail to
> (automated distribution):
>   <concise@concise.level-7.co.uk>
> as a message:
>   start
>   help cug-info
> You can also contact CONCISE helpdesk at:
>   <helpdesk@concise.level-7.co.uk>

Some introductory info can also be obtained from archives on <listserv@ncsuvm.cc.ncsu.edu> by sending message (automated retrieval): GET E-EUROPE FILE09

Title: NETLIB
Resource Type: Software Archive

NETLIB is a key source for scientific, engineering, and mathematical libraries for numerical computer programming. Most public-domain software libraries are archived here. Unlike some public domain software, everything in this archive is of generally high quality. Many of the libraries also include excellent documentation.

Maintainer affiliation/institution: Oak Ridge National Laboratory

File format: Text
Number of files: Thousands
Data format: Source code and documentation
File size: Varies

Primary/authoritative source: E-mail to netlib@ornl.gov
Instructions for access: Similar syntax to LISTSERV. Send a `info` or `send index` command first.
Additional sources/methods:

1. European users should use the NETLIB mirror in Oslo via E-mail to `net-lib@nac.no`.
2. Anonymous FTP to several locations, including `att.research.com`.

Last known revision date: Unknown
Number of revisions to date: Unknown
Next planned revision/planned frequency of revision: As software is updated or new items become available

Copyright restriction: Some items are restricted. Retrieve individual items for details.

Experience level: Domain knowledge and programming ability is required to make use of these resources.
Target audience: Engineers, scientists, engineers, students, etc.
Environment applicability: Mostly FORTRAN code; generally intended to work on any hardware platform with any FORTRAN compiler (but your mileage may vary). A growing quantity of C and C++ code. Also some assembly language code.

Content sample: (from `info`)

```
lib    eispack
for    eigenvalues and eigenvectors
#      A collection of Fortran subroutines that compute the eigenvalues
#      and eigenvectors of nine classes of matrices. The package can
#      determine the eigensystems of complex general, complex Hermitian,
#      real general, real symmetric, real symmetric band, real symmetric
#      tridiagonal, special real tridiagonal, generalized real, and
#      generalized real symmetric matrices. In addition, there are two
#      routines which use the singular value decomposition to solve
#      certain least squares problems.
by     NATS Project at Argonne National Laboratory.
prec   double
```

see   seispack
rel   excellent
age   stable
master   ornl.gov

Note: NETLIB can also be used to search for keywords through the files it keeps. Send a `send info` message for details.

Title: Not Just Cows: A Guide to Internet/BITNET resources in agriculture and related sciences
Resource Type: List

This is a useful list for identifying resources of relevance to agriculture and related areas. The list includes newsgroups, mailing lists, OPACs with agriculture collections, databases, and other Internet-accessible items.

Author: Wilfred Drew
Author affiliation/institution: Morrisville College of Agriculture and Technology
Author E-mail: drewwe@snymorva.cs.snymor.edu
Author USPS address: P.O. Box 902, Morrisville, NY 13408
Author telephone number: (315) 684-6055

File format: Text
Number of files: One
Data format: Formatted list
File size: 89KB, 2,595 lines

Primary/authoritative source: `ftp hydra.uwo.ca`
Instructions for access: `cd libsoft; get agguide.txt` (text file) or `get agguide.wp` (binary WordPerfect file)
Additional sources/methods: `sunsite.unc.edu:pub/academic/agriculture/sustainable_agriculture/documents/Not-Just-Cows`

Last known revision date: May 1992
Number of revisions to date: 0
Next planned revision/planned frequency of revision: Unknown

Copyright restriction: None

Experience level: Most resources may be used by novices, but specialized information may not be readily understandable by non-experts
Target audience: People interested in all aspects of agriculture, including farming, gardening, and agricultural science

Sample entry:

AG-EXP-L@NDSUVM1
Discussion of the use of Expert
Systems in Agricultural production
and management.
BITNET: LISTSERV@NDSUVM1
Internet: LISTSERV@VM1.NODAK.EDU

Title: Russian Mail Server
Resource Type: Mail server

A resource containing files in Russian (mostly) and English relevant to business, economic, and agricultural development in Russia and the Commonwealth of Independent States (CIS).

Author: Serge Vakulenko
Author affiliation/institution: UNTIC (Scientific & Technical Information Center of Russia)
Author E-mail: Vak@kiae.su
Author postal address: 14 Smolnaya Street, Moscow 125493, Russia
Author telephone number: +7-095-456 8079 (voice); +7-095-456 7521 (fax); 411901 FRAM SU (Telex)

File format: Text, but many in Russian
Number of files: Hundreds
Data format: Plain text

Primary/authoritative source: `Mailserv@kiae.su`
Instructions for access: Send commands via email. Try `help` and `index`.
Additional sources/methods: None

Last known revision date: Unknown
Number of revisions to date: Unknown
First issue: 1992
Next planned revision/planned frequency of revision: new items are added frequently

Copyright restriction: Materials may be freely distributed.

Target audience: CIS residents and people interested in CIS issues
Environment applicability: Appropriate decoding and display software may be needed for Russian texts.

Title: Social Science and Polling Data
Resource Type: Database

UNC makes multiple databases available that enable users to search for poll results. They also maintain an archive of social science data at the same site. This is an excellent resource for people who are starting a research project or who are interested in tracking public opinion.

Maintainer: David Sheaves, Institute for Research in Social Science (IRSS)
Maintainer affiliation/institution: University of North Carolina at Chapel Hill
Maintainer E-mail: uirdss@uncvm1.oit.unc.edu
Maintainer telephone number: (919) 966-3348
File formats: SPIRES database
Number of files: Ten files on poling data, other files are available
Data format: Fielded text
File size: Unknown

Primary/authoritative source: `tn3270 uncvm1.oit.unc.edu`
Instructions for access: Log on as `irss1` or `irss2`. Supply `irss` as the password. Follow the on-screen instructions.
Additional sources/methods: None known

Last known revision date: June 1992
Number of revisions to date: Unknown
First issue: Unknown
Next planned revision/planned frequency of revision: Unknown
Revision note: I could not find any Harris poll data for after mid-1991, or *USA Today* data for after mid-1992.

Cost: None
Copyright restriction: None

Experience level: The data assume some familiarity with basic social science and statistical techniques.
Target audience: Researchers and people curious about public opinion
Environment applicability: There is no good way to capture or print data for non-UNC users. The best path would be to capture the screen data (difficult using tn3270, or make incremental screen dumps (tedious).

Title: Sustainable Agriculture
Resource Type: FTP site and Gopher server

This is a collection of information relating to sustainable agriculture, horticulture, alternative farming systems, etc. The archive brings together expertise and materials from all over the United States and abroad.

Maintainer E-mail: ftpkeeper@sunsite.unc.edu

File format: Various, including plain text, WAIS databases, and software
Number of files: Many hundreds
File size: Various

Primary/authoritative source: `gopher sunsite.unc.edu`
Instructions for access: Select the `Sunsite Archives` menu, then the `Sustainable Agriculture` menu.
Additional sources/methods: `ftp sunsite.unc.edu. cd pub/agriculture`; use `ls`, `cd`, and `get` to identify and retrieve files

Last known revision date: March 1993
Number of revisions to date: Unknown
First issue: 1992
Next planned revision/planned frequency of revision: Materials are added frequently as they become available

Copyright restriction: Some items have restrictions. Different items have different copyright notices.

Experience level: Some materials are more appropriate for people well-versed in agricultural methods
Target audience: Several, ranging from home gardeners to farmers to agricultural scientists. There are a number of materials from cooperative extension services at universities.

Content sample (bibliographic item):

1A0b2,MUNOR,1983,
19831A0b2
1A0b2
Munoz, R. D.
Small family farms in Mississippi and Tennessee: a comparison of small farm definitions.
Agric Econ Res Report - MI Agric & Forestry Exp Stn, MSU Jun 1983 (141) 29 p.

Note: Although most materials are available via anonymous FTP, the Gopher method provides a much easier method for interaction with and selection of resources.

9
Individual Efforts

You Can Be an Information Service Provider, Too

This chapter does not do justice to the large number of excellent resources that are created and sustained by individuals. The majority of materials in this book are the result of the hard work of individuals or small groups. This chapter contains a few items that are more closely associated with individuals than any particular group or interest area. Essentially, they are miniature resource guides that are slanted toward the interests of their providers, rather than trying to please a larger audience.

Do you have an area of interest or expertise? Then you can be an information service provider, too! The resources in this chapter are somewhat more formal than most, because they have been through multiple revisions and are available from a stable source. You do not need to go to that effort, however—create a "list of lists" or other information resource and make it available to an Internet community. If it's useful to others, you might be asked to make it more widely available. You will be sure to get feedback from the other community members regardless.

The most important thing about becoming an information service provider is to remember that you have something to offer. No one else has the background and interests you do, and no one else sees through your eyes. If you think your point of view might be worthwhile for someone else to hear, then go ahead and share it—that's what the network is there for.

Title: BABEL: A Listing of Computer Oriented Abbreviations and Acronyms
Resource Type: List

A necessary desk reference for the modern world. This list spells out the many acronyms encountered during network navigation, in conversation, and in the media. The list is frequently updated.

Author: Irving Kind
Author affiliation/institution: Unknown
Author E-mail: ikind@mcimail.com
Author postal address: c/o K & D, One Church Lane, Baltimore, MD 21208

File format: Text
Number of files: One
Data format: List
File size: 89KB, 2258 lines

Primary/authoritative source: ftp ftp.temple.edu

Instructions for access: cd pub/info/help-net; ascii; get babel93a.txt (the exact filename is updated as new releases are made available)
Additional sources/methods: None
Last known revision date: January, 1993
Number of revisions to date: Dozens
First issue: 1989
Next planned revision/planned frequency of revision: Three times per year

Copyright restriction: None (see notice at top of file)

Experience level: General, but many of the terms are technical

Content sample (some of the G's):

GIGO	Garbage In, Garbage Out
GIS	Geographical Information System
GKS	Graphical Kernal System
G/L	General Ledger
GLM	General Linear Models
GLY	Glossary (file name extension) [Microsoft Word]
GMT	Greenwich Mean Time
GND	System Ground
GNU	Gnu's Not Unix (operating system)

Title: Information Sources: The Internet and Computer-Mediated Communication
Resource Type: Resource guide

Single-line entries for scores of general Internet resources and resources of interest to communication scholars. The brief format of this list makes it very useful for giving new users an idea as to "what's out there," and also makes it a good reference source for more experienced users.

Author: John December
Author affiliation/institution: Rensselaer Polytechnic Institute
Author E-mail: decemj@rpi.edu
Author postal address: 154 Third St., Troy, NY 12180-4039
Author telephone number: (518) 271-8469

File format: Text
Number of files: One
Data format: List
File size: 30KB, 513 lines

Primary/authoritative source: `ftp ftp.rpi.edu`
Instructions for access: `cd pub/communications; ascii; get internet-cmc`
Additional sources/methods: No other authoritative sources, but this list is carried by some other FTP sites and Gopher servers.

Last known revision date: March 1993
Number of revisions to date: Two major
First issue: May 1991
Next planned revision/planned frequency of revision: Monthly

Copyright restriction: "Permission to use, copy, or distribute this document for non-commercial, educational purposes is hereby granted, provided that this copyright and permission notice appear in all copies." (from the file)

Experience level: Familiarity with Internet tools is assumed
Target audience: General, but with an emphasis on human communication aspects of computer networking

Sample entries:

Language/Culture	Anonymous FTP Host	File or Directory
Artwork	sunsite.unc.edu	pub/multimedia/pictures/OTIS/
Computer Abbreviations	ftp.temple.edu	pub/info/help-net/babel93a.txt
Computer Jargon	pit-manager.mit.edu	pub/jargon/
Computer Underground	ftp.eff.org	pub/cud/papers/meyer
Cyberspace & Law	ftp.eff.org	pub/cud/papers/cyberspace
Electronic Text	guvax.georgetown.edu	cpet_projects_in_electronic_text/
Gutenberg Project Texts	quake.think.com	pub/etext/
Internet Glossary	nic.merit.edu	documents/fyi/fyi_18.txt
IRC Community	ftp.eff.org	pub/cud/papers/electropolis
Net Etiquette Guide	ftp.sura.net	pub/nic/internet.literature/ netiquette.txt
Online Book Initiative	world.std.com	obi/README
Post-Gutenberg	infolib.murdoch.edu.au	pub/jnl/harnad.jnl
Privacy	pit-manager.mit.edu	pub/usenet/alt.privacy/
Smileys	ux1.cso.uiuc.edu	doc/misc/smiley
Smileys-Sanderson	ftp.uu.net	usenet/comp.sources.misc/ volume23/smiley/part01.Z

Contents (from the file):
    Section -1-   THE INTERNET AND SERVICES
    Section -2-   INFORMATION SERVICES/ELECTRONIC PUBLICATIONS
    Section -3-   SOCIETIES AND ORGANIZATIONS
    Section -4-   NEWSGROUPS
    Section -5-   SELECTED BIBLIOGRAPHY

Title: Internet Services List
Resource Type: List

An excellent and far-ranging list of resources of various types. Several dozen topics, each with one or more Internet sites that offer related services.

Author: Scott Yanoff
Author affiliation/institution: University of Wisconsin, Milwaukee
Author E-mail: yanoff@csd4.csd.uwm.edu

File format: Text
Number of files: One
Data format: Text
File size: 23KB, 471 lines (as of March 1993)

Primary/authoritative source: `ftp csd4.csd.uwm.edu`
Instructions for access: `cd pub; get inet.services.txt`
Additional sources/methods: Newsgroup `alt.internet.services`. Also a Gopher
server to the `csd4.csd.uwm.edu`

Number of revisions to date: Unknown
First issue: September 1991
Next planned revision/planned frequency of revision: every 2 weeks

Copyright restriction: None

Experience level: General
Target audience: General
Environment applicability: Most services employ the `telnet` command

Sample entry:

Agricultural Info.,   telnet psupen.psu.edu or telnet 128.118.36.5
Family Issues,   PENpages (Login: PNOTPA)
Food & Nutrition,   telnet caticsuf.csufresno.edu or telnet 129.8.100.15
and Environment   CSU Freso ATI-NET (Login: super)
   telnet eureka.clemson.edu or telnet 130.127.8.3
   CUFAN (Clemson U Forestry & Ag. Net.) (Login: PUBLIC)
   ftp ftp.sura.net (get file pub/nic/agricultural.list,
   it contains agricultural email lists & services.)
   offers: Agricultural info (livestock reports, current market prices, etc.)

Title: Maasinfo
Resource Type: Resource Guide

A collection of various resources. There is something here for everyone, but the format
makes it somewhat difficult to spot what you need immediately.

Author: Robert Elton Maas
Author affiliation/institution: Sam Houston State University

File format: Text

Number of files: Six
Data format: Text
File size: Varies from 2 to 65KB

Primary/authoritative source: `Telnet shsu.edu`
Instructions for access: `cd maasinfo; ls` and `get` for desired files
Additional sources/methods: None

Last known revision date: February 1992
Number of revisions to date: Unknown
First issue: Unknown
Next planned revision/planned frequency of revision: Unknown

Copyright restriction: Note that most of these files are published as "trivial shareware." If they are worth more than a dollar to you, please do some nice favor of comparable value in return, such as supplying answers to SQWAs (see below). See MaasInfo.TopIndex for details of "trivial shareware" policy. (from the top of each file)

Experience level: Most entries assume general Internet knowledge
Target audience: General

Content sample:

NEWFAQ.NEWUSEN—Newsgroups: news.announce.newusers, Answers to Frequently Asked Questions (for new users), From: spaf@cs.purdue.EDU (Gene Spafford), Original-from: jerry@eagle.UUCP (Jerry Schwarz). This document discusses some questions and topics that occur repeatedly on USENET. They frequently are submitted by new users, ... If you don't like these answers let spaf@cs.purdue.edu know. ftp PIT-MANAGER.MIT.EDU (18.72.1.58)   pub/usenet/news.announce.newusers/Answers_to_Frequently_Asked_Questions

Title: Zamfield's Wonderfully Incomplete, Complete Internet BBS List
Resource Type: List

The name says most of it. BBSs, or Bulletin Board Systems, usually have a narrower topic and are more interactive than CWISs. Most BBSs are maintained by their users or by an individual, so it is important to honor the wishes of the maintainers—many BBSs operate under fragile circumstances.

Author: Thomas A. Kreeger
Author affiliation/institution: Mississippi State University
Author E-mail: zamfield@dune.ee.msstate.edu

File format: Text
Number of files: One
Data format: Formatted list

File size: 31KB, 965 lines

Primary/authoritative source: `ftp quartz.rutgers.edu`
Instructions for access: `cd pub/internet/sites; get internet-bbslist.Z`
Additional sources/methods: posted periodically to alt.bbs.internet

Last known revision date: September 1992
Number of revisions to date: Unknown
First issue: Unknown
Next planned revision/planned frequency of revision: Issued irregularly

Copyright restriction: None

Target audience: General

Content sample:

OuluBox (Finnish)   tolsun.oulu.fi   box
   —   130.231.96.16

   —   Can set English as preferred language,
   —   said to switch to Finnish at the most
   —   inconvenient time. IRC

10
Books

Who Needs a Book?

If you have read carefully to this point in *Directory of Directories on the Internet,* you may think of the concept of needing another book absurd. If so, you are probably not among the millions of new network users. What this book does not provide to any great extent, and what the network itself hardly provides at all, is instructions on the mechanics of the Internet.

Telnet and FTP are nice words, and they might even be the names of the commands you use to navigate the network. But there is more to successful Internet-ing than just going places and retrieving stuff. What do you do with the materials you retrieve to your local system? What are the concepts behind the Internet? How can you extend your reach beyond the Internet to other networks? What are some futures of the Internet? These might be called "meta-networking questions," or questions about networking. There are few network-accessible resources that answer these questions in any but a terse manner, but several books that provide more complete answers.

Most books having to do with the Internet suffer from a short useful life span. Many have annual updates. "So," you say, "why should I have an out-of-date book, when I can just retrieve a file via anonymous FTP, or from my local friendly mailing list." Good question, to which the answer is: Look at the file date on your favorite network-accessible resource. The chances are quite good that it is no more current than the average book about Internet. The chances are fair that it does not have an index, table of contents, examples, and/or complete information about the materials it describes. This doesn't make it any better or worse quality than a book, but it may make it somewhat better for quick reference purposes and somewhat worse for detailed reference or learning.

Many network-accessible resources have advantages over books. The most obvious advantage is that they tend to be free, while books cost money. Some of the best are updated every week or two—more frequently than any book. This chapter points to some books (and one list of books) that are more complete than any network-accessible resource on the same topic area. You decide.

One of the futures of computer networking has to do with the changing nature of the book. As network-accessible guides become more carefully prepared, they become more similar in nature to a book (there are some examples of resources which are in both worlds, such as Kovac's and Strangelove's work on pages 49–51 and 58–59). As books about the Internet make greater use of the Internet's resource discovery tools and ability to instantly access remote resources, the changes between every edition will become greater, until it may be reasonable to release incremental changes or editions via the Internet.

This is an exciting concept for both the consumers and producers of books and is linked to the ongoing emphasis of the Internet as a tool for commerce. New methods for the production and dissemination of knowledge are emerging as a result of the synergy between network resource providers, publishers, authors, and the Internet community.

Title: Recent Internet Books (RFC1432)
Resource Type: Bibliography (Annotated)

This is a useful listing of recent books related to Internet. Quarterman provides a description and assessment of the content of twenty-seven books.

Author: John Quarterman
Author affiliation/institution: Matrix Information and Directory Services, Inc. (MIDS)
Author email: mids@tic.com
Author postal address: 1106 Clayton Lane, Suite 500W, Austin, TX 78723
Author telephone number: (512) 451-7602

File format: Text
Number of files: One
Data format: Text and bibliographic citations
File size: 27KB, 843 lines

Primary/authoritative source: `ftp nic.ddn.mil`
Instructions for access: `cd rfc; ascii; get rfc1432.txt`
Additional sources/methods: Many other FTP sites (and some Gopher servers) offer directories containing RFCs.

First issue: March 1993
Next planned revision/planned frequency of revision: As new materials become available

Copyright restriction: None

Experience level: All levels
Target audience: All audiences
Environment applicability: General Internet users

Sample entry:

> Clifford Stoll, The Cuckoo's Egg: Tracking a Spy
> Through the Maze of Computer Espionage, p. 332,
> Doubleday, New York, 1989. $19.95. ISBN
> 0-385-24946-2 (alk. paper).

A spy novel, except it's true: a first person account by a down-on-his-luck Berkeley astronomer who with others tracked down a KGB network spy. Despite its necessary concentration on cracking, still a readable introduction to what the Internet is about.

Note: A few of the books in the RFC had not yet become available at the time of release.

This particular RFC is also available as `ftp.tic.com:matrix/news/ rfc1432.txt` or via Gopher to `gopher.tic.com`.

Books About the Internet

This list does not include all books about the Internet, just those that are intended to direct network users to other resources and/or their use. It seems likely that in the short term the growth in the number of books might proportionally match the growth of the number of Internet nodes. There are at least as many books forthcoming in 1993 as there were in the second half of 1992.

Keep informed of which books are best suited to your own needs by following mailing lists and newsgroups where people who share your interests meet.

Frey, Donnalyn; Adams, Rick. 1991. *!%@: A Directory of Electronic Mail Addressing and Networks*. Sebastopol, CA: O'Reilly & Associates. 436 pages. ISBN: 0-937-17515-3.

Smarter E-mail systems and increased resource sharing across networks has made this book less important than it initially was to Internet users. It remains an excellent reference tool for finding the pathway to an address that your E-mail system can not find. It also server to de-mystify some of the esoterica of E-mail addressing schemes.

Krol, Ed. 1992. *The Whole Internet: User's Guide & Catalog*. Sebastopol, CA: O'Reilly & Associates. 400 pages. IBSN: 1-56592-025-2.

This is perhaps the best general guide to the Internet for those with the drive to become expert network navigators. The book is full of examples and written in plain English. It serves as a reference guide for more experienced navigators and is the closest thing to a textbook for a course on networking with Internet.

LaQuey, Tracy. 1993. *The Internet Companion*. Reading, MA: Addison-Wesley. 205 pages. ISBN: 0-201-62224-6.

This is the only book for networks I am aware of that really will fit in the average pocket (though it might stick out of the top a bit). There are some concrete things to try and good examples, but the book is mostly *about* the network. It serves as an accessible introduction to the networked world and gives new users many good places to start.

Marine, April; Kirkpatric, Susan; Neou, Vivian; Ward, Carol. 1992. *Internet: Getting Started*. Menlo Park, CA: SRI International. 380 pages. ISBN: 0-9444604-15-3.

Information about how to get connected to the network. Includes contact lists for Internet connectivity providers and a description of how the Internet works. The table of contents is available via anonymous FTP as `ftp.nisc.sri.com:netinfo/internet- getting-started-contents`.

Quarterman, John S. 1990. *The Matrix: Computer Networks and Conferencing Systems Worldwide*. Bedford, MA: Digital Press. 746 pages. ISBN: 0-13-565607-9.

This monumental effort is still a key reference for getting information about the hundreds of computer networks that exist worldwide. Not all networks can connect to the Internet, and many do not share its capabilities. Some of the information contained in the book is no longer current. The first half is about networking, and the second half is a directory to all known computer networks as of 1990.

Tennant, Roy; Ober, John; Lipow, Anne O. 1992. *Crossing the Internet Threshold: An Instructional Handbook*. San Carlos, CA: Library Solutions Press. 141 pages. ISBN: 1-882208-01-3.

This book is directed primarily at network trainers. It includes useful information on what topics are appropriate for network beginners and many short summaries of network concepts.

11
Miscellaneous

The Internet Allows *Everything* to be Aimed at a Narrow Audience

This chapter lists resources that do not fit into any of the other chapters. This does not mean that they cover strange and far away things, as the word "miscellaneous" might imply. Rather, the resources in this chapter demonstrate the extent to which a document with a narrow purpose may be just as accessible to the end-user as items that have a more general appeal.

Compare this "narrowcasting" quality of the Internet to, for example, a bookstore. Bookstores have limited space and have a need to sell items they have on their shelves (as opposed to just storing them). This means that bookstores must carry only those items that are likely to have appeal for a significant proportion of their patrons. On the Internet, though, there is little overhead for storage, and the number of times a resource is accessed does not affect the storage overhead. With the Internet, things are different. FTP sites, Gopher services, CWISs, and so forth—the places where Internet resources are stored—do not need to hold everything for a particular user group. Instead, they can focus in on whatever is of interest to the site maintainers.

Authors and creators of network resources often did not start out to be information providers. Instead, they simply generated a listing or guide to something they were familiar with and made it available to others. It might have been posted to a mailing list or put up for anonymous FTP or Gopher retrieval. The fact that someone creates a resource or document of any kind means that it can be distributed to the Internet community with almost no more effort than it took to produce the item in the first place. Stated alternatively, once you have created something, the Internet provides you a way to distribute that something easily. If people like it, they'll ask for more, or a newer version, and you will have the option to comply.

Contrast this process again with the production of regular books: The Internet enables what we might call "micro-publishing," in which people produce items for a small audience. The difference is that micro-publishing a book is expensive and might be costly—it's also difficult to tell your target audience about the book. With the Internet, the distribution is almost free (provided you are already connected), and additional copies cost you nothing.

Network users have noticed a strange phenomenon that results from the "narrowcasting" and "micro-publishing" capabilities of the Internet. This is the phenomenon of solving a problem by identifying it. If you, as a network user, notice that there is something missing or undocumented or difficult to use in a resource, or realize that there is no coherent listing of a particular type of resource, you can solve the problem just by listing the resources, or specifying the problems with the resource, or describing the troubles you had (with solutions, hopefully).

The Internet brings armchair philosophy to a new level: if you, as a network user, can cogently state what needs to be done you will have taken significant steps toward doing it. If you cannot, it may be that either the resource is better than you thought or (more like-ly) you are trying to exceed the intended scope of that resource.

Enjoy these miscellaneous resources. Recall that they might be the major topic of discussion in another book or online forum. And think about the capabilities of the Internet to enable self-empowerment for its users.

Title: Computer-Readable Dictionaries
Resource Type: Dictionaries

This FTP site contains a number of word lists in various languages. The lists do not contain definitions of words, just single-line entries. Most are terms in general use in the language, although several contain jargon terms or short phrases.

Maintainer: Gene Spafford
Maintainer affiliation/institution: Purdue University
Maintainer E-mail: spaf@cs.purdue.edu

File formats: compressed text files
Number of files: 190
Data format: Plain text
File size: Varies from 1KByte to over 1MB each. Total is about 12MB

Primary/authoritative source: `ftp cs.purdue.edu`
Instructions for access: `cd pub/pcert/dict`; use `ls` to view available files
Additional sources/methods: A similar collection is available at `black.ox.ac.uk` (see page 78).

Last known revision date: August 1992
Number of revisions to date: Unknown, but about six different dates are found in the 190 file creation dates.
First issue: September 1991
Next planned revision/planned frequency of revision: as new files are identified

Copyright restriction: Unlimited distribution

Content detail: This is the listing of language subdirectories:

aussie
danish
dutch
english
finnish
french
german
italian
japanese

    misc
    names
    norwegian
    swedish

Note: The "names" subdirectory contains listings of common names in various languages.

Title: Coombspapers Databank
Resource Type: Electronic texts

"COOMBSPAPERS DATA BANK was established on 3 December 1991 to act as an electronic repository of the social science & humanities papers, offprints, departmental publications, bibliographies, directories, abstracts of theses and other high-grade research material produced (or deposited) at the Research Schools of Pacific Studies and Social Sciences, Australian National University, Canberra" (from coombs.anu.edu.au:/coombspapers/coombs.INDEX).

Maintainer: T. Matthew Ciolek
Maintainer affiliation/institution: Australian National University
Maintainer E-mail: Coombspapers@coombs.anu.edu.au
Author postal address: Coombs Computing Unit, RSPacS/RSSS, Australian National University, Canberra, Australia
Author telephone number: +61-6-249-4602

File format: Text and compressed text
Number of files: 288
Data format: Text
File size: Varies from several KB to several hundred KB

Primary/authoritative source: `ftp coombs.anu.edu.au`
Instructions for access: `cd coombspapers; ls` and `get` to identify useful papers. A good place to start is with `coombs.INDEX`.
Additional sources/methods: None on the Internet. Some materials may be available in print form elsewhere.

Last known revision date: March 1993
Number of revisions to date: Unknown
First issue: Unknown
Next planned revision/planned frequency of revision: as new materials become available

Copyright restriction: Copyright is generally retained by the author

Experience level: Various
Target audience: Mostly academic

Content summary: (from coombs.intro)

Within the COOMBSPAPERS collection there are materials contributed by the following departments and units of the RSSS/RSPacS.

Aboriginal History Journal
Anthropology
Asian History
Australian Dictionary of Biography
Cartography Unit
Contemporary China Centre
Coombs Computing Unit
Demography
Economic History
Economic Policy Research Centre
Federalism Research Centre
International Relations
Linguistics
Modern Economic History of Southeast Asia Project
National Centre for Development Studies
Pacific Manuscripts Bureau
Peace Research Centre
Philosophy
Political Science
Political and Social Change
Prehistory
RSPacS Director's Unit
RSSS Director's Unit
Social Science Data Archives
Sociology
Strategic and Defence Studies Centre
Thai-Yunnan Project
Urban Research Project

Getting Connected and Public-Access Sites

There are a number of resources that help you to find out how to get connected to the Internet and where to get public-access Internet services (for fee or not). See pages 110–111 for entries for *The Internet: Getting Started* and *The Whole Internet,* books with pointers for getting connected to the Internet. The items in this section are listed alphabetically by title.

The Network Provider Referral List

The National Science Foundation maintains this list of Internet service providers. It is available by FTP or mail server. A shorter file lists some international providers. Note that this source does not reflect the growing number of commercial service providers that are a likely source for connectivity for small businesses, libraries, and other institutions. Instead, it lists only mid-level and regional links to NSFNet.

1. FTP to `nnsc.nsf.net`; `cd nsfnet`; `ascii`; `get referral-list` or `get referral-international`
2. E-mail to `info-server@nnsc.nsf.net` with this text:

   ```
   request: Nsfnet
   topic: referral-list
   request: end
   ```

nixpub listing

This list is posted frequently to the newsgroups alt.bbs, comp.bbs, and comp.misc. It is maintained by Phil Eschallier <phil@bts.com>. Over 130 public access (fee and no fee) Unix sites are listed. Data include the system name and location, a telephone number, whether a cost is involved, and the parameters for your modem. A short version or more detailed long version is available. Retrievable by:

1. FTP to `ashley.cs.widener.edu`; `cd pub/nixpub`; `ascii`; `get long` or `get short`
2. To receive regular updates subscribe to the `nixpub` mailing list. Send E-mail to `nixpub-list-request@bts.com`

PDIAL

Public Dialup Internet Access List, or PDIAL, is a listing of public access Unix sites maintained by Peter Kaminksi <kaminski@netcom.com>. Available via several methods:

1. Send E-mail to `info-deli-server@netcom.com` with the subject field `send pdial`. To subscribe for regular updates, send `subscribe pdial`. Responses are generated automatically, with the E-mail's message text being ignored.
2. Posted regularly to the newsgroups alt.internet.access.wanted, alt.bbs.lists, and news.answers
3. FTP to several sites (have Archie search for the filename `pdial.txt`)

Title: Internet Bibliography
Resource Type: Bibliography

This is a nice source of electronic and print resources pertaining to network use in general. Some citations are briefly annotated.

Author: Mary Jensen
Author affiliation/institution: University of South Dakota
Author E-mail: Mjensen@charlie.usd.edu

File format: Text
Number of files: One
Data format: Bibliography
File size: 104 entries, 415 lines, 19KB

Primary/authoritative source: `ftp liberty.uc.wlu.edu`
Instructions for access: `cd pub/lawlib; get internet.bibl`
Additional sources/methods: None

Last known revision date: August 1992
Number of revisions to date: Unknown
First issue: Unknown
Next planned revision/planned frequency of revision: None

Copyright restriction: None

Target audience: General

Notes: Some citations are not complete.

Sample entry:

Shapiro, Norman Z. and Robert H. Anderson. Toward an ethics and etiquette for electronic mail (Rand Corp. 1985). A lot of good ideas for making network communications more enjoyable and efficient.

Title: Project Hermes
Resource Type: Electronic texts

This resource includes the full text of U.S. Supreme Court decisions. Decisions are made available electronically only hours after they are rendered by the court.

Corporate Author: U.S. Supreme Court
Maintainer: Case Western Reserve University (CWRU), EDUCOM, and the National Public Telecomputing Network (NPTN)
Maintainer E-mail: aa584@cleveland.freenet.edu

File format: Text and word processor
Number of files: Over 1,000
Data format: Text
File size: From 1KB to several hundred KB

Primary/authoritative source: `ftp ftp.cwru.edu`
Instructions for access: `cd hermes; ls`, `cd` and `get` to identify and retrieve files
Additional sources/methods: A WAIS database for Hermes exists (`supreme-court.src`). Project Hermes is accessible via Gopher, also.

Last known revision date: March 1993
First issue: 1990
Next planned revision/planned frequency of revision: As new materials become available

Copyright restriction: "Permission is hereby granted to download, reproduce, or re-post any of the Supreme Court opinion files found on this system PROVIDED NO CHANGES OR EDITING ARE MADE TO THE SUBJECT MATERIAL. We would greatly appreciate it if source credit were given to Case Western Reserve University." (from `hermes/README.FIRST`)

Experience level: The materials are written for people willing to read through legal documents, but they contain a good proportion of plain English prose.
Target audience: Anyone who wants the text of court decisions
Environment applicability: Word Perfect and other word processor formats are available.

Content extract (from `hermes/ascii/92-6455.ZA.filt`):

SUPREME COURT OF THE UNITED STATES
JERRY WAYNE SEWELL, II
92-6455   v.   UNITED STATES

JAMES EDWIN SHERROD
92-6484   v.   UNITED STATES

JERRY WAYNE SEWELL, Sr.
92-6591   v.   UNITED STATES

on petitions for writs of certiorari to the united states court of appeals for the fifth circuit   Nos. 92-6455, 92-6484 and 92-6591. Decided February 22, 1993

The petitions for writs of certiorari are denied.
Justice White, with whom Justice Blackmun joins, dissenting.
These petitions raise yet again the question whether waste by-products that are not ingestible or marketable may be included in calculating the weight of a -mixture or substance containing a detectable amount of . . . meth- amphetamine- for purposes of 2D1.1 of the United States Sentencing Commission Guidelines Manual (Nov. 1991). (...)

Title: A Cruise of the Internet
Resource Type: Software

This automated tutorial and tour of Internet resources requires that you use a Macintosh or PC with Windows that is connected to the Internet. Novice network navigators are given a guided "cruise" of some general-purpose Internet resources and taught how to use them. This is a good resource to have available in public-access computer sites.

Authors: Steve Burdick in collaboration with Laura Kelleher and Mark Davis-Craig
Author affiliation/institution: Merit, Inc.
Author E-mail: cruise2feedback@merit.edu

File format: Binary
Number of files: One
Data format: Binary
File size: 1.4MB (Windows); 2.0MB (Macintosh)

Primary/authoritative source: `ftp nic.merit.edu`
Instructions for access: cd resources; `cd cruise.mac` or `cd cruise.dos; ls` to identify current filename. A `readme` file is available in each subdirectory that specifies required resources to run the Cruise.
Additional sources/methods: None

Last known revision date: March 1993
Number of revisions to date: One major, several minor
First issue: 1991
Next planned revision/planned frequency of revision: Unknown

Copyright restriction: Copyright 1992, Merit Network, Inc., Information Services

Experience level: Novice
Environment applicability: Requires that your PC with Windows or Macintosh be connected directly to the Internet.

Title: Internet Tour
Resource Type: Software

The Internet Tour is a HyperCard stack which demonstrates some of the resources available over the Internet. The stack includes history, sample E-mail, FTP, and telnet sessions, and a glossary. Local information may be added using HyperCard, making this an ideal resource for distribution with other local networking documentation. It is a nice way to introduce new users to the Internet.

Corporate Author: National Science Foundation (U.S.)
Author E-mail: Nnsc@nnsc.nsf.net

File format: Binhexed binary
Number of files: One
Data format: HyperCard stack
File size: 575KB

Primary/authoritative source: `ftp nnsc.nsf.net`
Instructions for access: `Binary; get Internet-Tour4.0.2.sit.hqx` (or whichever the current version number is).

Additional sources/methods: None

Last known revision date: March 1993
Number of revisions to date: Three major
First issue: 1991
Next planned revision/planned frequency of revision: 1993

Copyright restriction: None

Experience level: Novice
Target audience: New network users
Environment applicability: Macintosh only

Note: This HyperCard stack can only be used on a Macintosh computer with version 2.0 or later of HyperCard. Your Mac does not need to have any network connection to run the Tour.

Title: U.S. Network Policies
Resource Type: FTP site

"Information about the policies and procedures established by the National Science Foundation Network (NSFNET) and its associated networks. These documents have been collected by the NSF Network Service Center (NNSC) (from INDEX)." The policies found in this directory are for networks located in the United States only.

Corporate maintainer: The National Science Foundation
Author E-mail: NSF Network Service Center <nnsc@nnsc.nsf.net>

File format: Text
Number of files: 81 network directories, each with one or more files containing policy information
Data format: Text
File size: Various, typically a few KB

Primary/authoritative source: `ftp nnsc.nsf.net`
Instructions for access: `cd policies-procedures`; use `ls` and `get` to identify and retrieve the policies of specific networks
Additional sources/methods: A mailservice is available for the same holdings. Send a message to `info-request@nnsc.nsf.net` with the following text to get started:

```
request: info
topic: help
```

Copyright restriction: Most materials are copyright-free, but use may be governed by the individual network who produced each document.
Target audience: Network users

Environment applicability: the majority of the content relates to TCP/IP networking in the U.S.

Content sample (from `nsf.net/nsfnet.policy`):

THE NSFNET BACKBONE SERVICES ACCEPTABLE USE POLICY
June 1992

GENERAL PRINCIPLE:

(1) NSFNET Backbone services are provided to support open research and education in and among US research and instructional institutions, plus research arms of for-profit firms when engaged in open scholarly communication and research. Use for other purposes is not acceptable.

12
Keeping Informed of Future Directions

Things Change at the Speed of Light

This chapter lists some of the resources you might access to keep informed of new network services and emerging policies or procedures. These are general resources—those which anyone who wants to keep informed might follow, but that will result in some materials not of interest to you.

An additional source of information about network changes should be your own group of colleagues. The people with whom you communicate through E-mail lists or newsgroups. The people who are creating and maintaining those resources of most interest to you.

As the saying goes, "Constant change is here to stay." This statement is at the foundation of the necessity for this book, and it also means that you, as a network consumer, need to have methods for keeping informed of changes to the availability of network resources.

Many things change. One of the more annoying things that can change is the reassignment of an Internet host name to a different IP address. This means that the numeric address you use may someday no longer work to access a particular resource, because the machine on which the resource is located has changed but the alphanumeric version of the name stays the same. For instance, the two host names `ftp.eff.org` and `gopher.eff.org` currently resolve to the same IP number, 192.88.144.4. Someday, though, those names might point to different IP numbers.

Another change has to do with the expansion of resources. New mailing lists, newsgroups, Gopher sites, and other types of resources are announced every week. You want to keep informed of those that might satisfy your needs.

A third type of change has to do with policy, organization, and legislation of the Internet. The Internet is experiencing some growing pains, and the fundamental rules are starting to change. A key change is the commercialization of the Internet: It is no longer against the rules, *de facto,* to charge money for Internet-based resources. Nor is it against the rules to do business over the Internet (again, *de facto*). It's still against the written policies of the NSFNet and most other Internet networks, but things are changing.

Another current issue is privacy. Data encryption standards, data snooping, and your system administrator's capability to read your E-mail are all topics that might have an immediate effect on your work.

Keep informed! Sample and identify some of the resources in which topics of importance to you are being discussed, and use them. Form a local user group or "discovery" mailing list.

It is equally important to be relaxed about new network resources. You will often hear of "vaporware" resources (things that are supposedly in the works, but do not yet exist). Be prepared to wait and be prepared to have a frustrating time using new resources. Do not place stock in announcements of things that are on the way or capabilities that will supposedly be added Real Soon Now. This is not cynical, it is pragmatic: Your own eyes and ears and fingers should be the judge of the usefulness of a resource.

One of the most exciting things about the Internet right now is the astounding growth it is experiencing. The number of users, hosts, and resources will continue to grow at a high rate. This means that today's new user will be, statistically, highly experienced in only a few months. It also means that your "current" knowledge of the Internet will not stay current for long.

Consider Internet resources as you would the daily news. You would not call yourself well informed if you only read one or two newspapers per year. Rather, you need to strive to keep yourself informed by actively seeking out new items of interest. Engage in the same pursuit with Internet resources, and you will be pleased at the ever-increasing reach of your electronic fingertips.

Title: Clearinghouse for Networked Information Discovery and Retrieval
Resource Type: Organization

CNIDR is the recipient of a three-year National Science Foundation (NSF) grant to work as an access point and organizing force for resources used for the identification and retrieval of network resources. Specifically, these are to include WAIS, Gopher, Archie, and other resources.

In early 1993 CNIDR released a beta-test version of freeWAIS. CNIDR is intending to be the authoritative source for future releases of WAIS software (see page 19).

Contacts: George Brett or Jane Smith
Contact E-mail: ghb@concert.net or jds@concert.net
Organization postal address: CNIDR, Center for Communications, MCNC, P.O. Box 12889, Research Triangle Park, NC 27709-2889
Organization telephone number: (919) 248-1886 or (919) 248-9213

Primary/authoritative source: `ftp ftp.cnidr.org`
Instructions for access: `cd pub`; use `ls` and `cd` to identify useful resources
Additional sources/methods: None

Last known revision date: March 1993
Number of revisions to date: One
First issue: Fall 1992
Next planned revision/planned frequency of revision: WAIS software will be updated frequently; other resources will be added.

Copyright restriction: See individual resources for copyright information.

Note: Currently, freeWAIS is the only available resource of interest.

Title: EFFector Online
Resource Type: Newsletter

The Electronic Frontier Foundation is devoted to making Cyberspace a safer place to live by pursuing legislation and acting as a civil liberties organization. EFFector Online is their newsletter. Current legislation, case studies, and announcements of general interest are made available to subscribers.

Publisher: The Electronic Frontier Foundation
Publisher E-mail: eff@eff.org
Publisher postal address: 666 Pennsylvania Ave. SE, Washington, DC 20003
Publisher telephone number: (202) 544-9237
ISSN: 1062-9424

File format: Text
Number of files: One per issue
Data format: Text
File size: Usually 200 to 400 lines

Primary/authoritative source: Usenet newsgroup comp.org.eff.news or by mailing list.
Instructions for access: Read the newsgroup. If you do not have Usenet access and want to receive every issue via E-mail, send a note to eff@eff.org asking to be subscribed.
Additional sources/methods: Current issues and archives are available via Gopher to gopher.eff.org or anonymous FTP to ftp.eff.org.

Number of revisions to date: Five volumes
First issue: May 1991
Next planned revision/planned frequency of revision: Twice per month

Copyright restriction: None, although some articles may have copyright restrictions.

Experience level: General
Target audience: People interested in the legal and ethical issues of the Internet

Content sample (From volume 5 number 7):

On April 21, Congressman Rick Boucher (D-VA) introduced legislation to create computer and networking applications to serve the education, library, and health care communities, and to promote access to government information. The bill, H.R. 1757, significantly expands on similar provisions found in last year's "Information Infrastructure and Technology Act" (often referred to as "Gore II," then-Senator Gore's follow-up to his NREN bill, the High Performance Computing Act ("HPCA")), and the Senate bill to promote U.S. competitiveness, S. 4.

Notes: Membership in EFF is available. See the newsletter, FTP, or Gopher site for details.

Title: The Internet Hunt
Resource Type: Contest

The Internet Hunt is a monthly production of an individual, Rick Gates. He creates questions of varying difficulty that are to be answered by individuals or teams. The questions are to be answered using only Internet resources.

The Hunt is good way to keep track of new and useful resources; assess your own network navigation skills; and find out what sort of questions can be answered using the Internet. As a training tool, this is an excellent place to find out about the breadth of information available on the Nets; practice using Internet resources by following known paths to answers; and quiz trainees.

Author: Rick Gates
Author affiliation/institution: University of California, Santa Barbara
Author E-mail: lb05gate@ucsbuxa.ucsb.edu
Author postal address: Directory of Library Automation; University of California Library, Santa Barbara, CA 93106
Author telephone number: (805) 893-7225

File format: Text
Number of files: One for contest questions, 1 for answers
Data format: Text
File size: Varies. The contest contains ten questions (sometimes with a bonus question), and the results include representative answers.

Primary/authoritative source: `ftp.cic.net` (anonymous FTP) and `gopher.cic.net` (Gopher server).

Posted monthly to several mailing lists including `pacs-l@uhupvm1.uh.edu` and `net-train@ubvm.cc.buffalo.edu`. Also to Usenet newsgroups `alt.bbs.internet` and `alt.internet.services`.

Instructions for access: via FTP `cd pub/net-guides/i-hunt`. Hunt questions and answers are filed in annual subdirectories with monthly filenames, for exemple: `1993/9304hunt.q` for questions from April 1993 and 1993/9304hunt.a for answers. Via Gopher, select `The Internet Hunt` menu.

Last known revision date: Monthly
Number of revisions to date: Seven
First issue: Fall 1992
Next planned revision/planned frequency of revision: Monthly

Copyright restriction: None

Experience level: Experienced network users (but anyone can try); also network trainees.
Environment applicability: Internet access is required to answer the questions

Content sample (the April 1993 Hunt):

THE HUNT

1. I have a note here about a "Higher Education Resources and Opportunities Database" operating in the U.S. finding positions for minorities and women. I'd really like to access this database. Do you know where I can find it?

2. I heard some network gurus talking about 'pinging' an address somewhere. What is ping, and what does it stand for?

3. What color is the carpet in the Main Transporter Lobby at Cyberion City?

4. I've developed a great resource that I'd like to register with the new Internic Directory of Directories. Can you tell me where I can find the registration form?

5. I need to send a letter to the Meteorology Department at the University of Edinburgh, in Scotland, U.K. Can you tell me what the address is please?

6. Where is the 8th Annual Conference on Computing and Philosophy being held?

7. To which date did U.S. President Bill Clinton extend cooperation with the European Atomic Energy Community?

8. Approximately how many persons lived in college dormitories in Ann Arbor, Michigan, U.S.A., in 1990?

9. I just returned from a short vacation in Havana. When I left, I paid my hotel bill with a major credit card. A friend told me that this was illegal, and I was liable for a fine. If this is true, how much is the fine?

10. What is the melting point of Tungsten?

Title: InterNIC Information Service
Resource Type: Information Service

This is a new service that is starting to draw together resources from other areas. As of early 1993, there are not many unique resources available here. If the InterNIC service keeps to its plan, however, this will soon be an important Internet resource.

"In cooperation with the Internet community, the National Science Foundation developed and released in the Spring of 1992 a solicitation for one or more Network Information Services Managers (NIS Manager(s)) to provide and/or coordinate services for the NSFNET community. As a result of this solicitation, three separate organizations were competitively selected to receive cooperative agreements in the three areas of Registration Services, Directory and Database Services, and Information Services."

"Together these three awards constitute the InterNIC. Network Solutions, Inc. (NSI) provides REGISTRATION services, AT&T provides DIRECTORY and DATABASE services, and General Atomics/CERFnet provides INFORMATION services" (from `is.internic.net:information-about-the-internic`).

Providers: Multiple
Provider affiliation/institution: General Atomics, CERFnet, AT&T, and NSI
Provider E-mail: admin@ds.internic.net
Provider telephone number: (908) 668-6587

File format: Multiple
Number of files: Thousands
Data format: Mostly text or PostScript
File size: Varies from a few kilobytes to over 1MB

Primary/authoritative source: Gopher to `ds.internic.net`
Instructions for access: Browse
Additional sources/methods: FTP to `is.internic.net` or `ds.internic.net` or `rs.internic.net` (holdings at these sites are not the same)

Last known revision date: March 1993
Number of revisions to date: Unknown
First issue: Fall 1992
Next planned revision/planned frequency of revision: Service expansions are planned for 1993

Copyright restriction: Some items have copyright restriction.

Experience level: General, with information areas targeted at specific experience levels.
Target audience: The general Internet community

Content sample (from Gopher to `ds.internic.net`):

InterNIC Information Services (General Atomics)

1. Welcome to the Info Source/
2. Info Source Table of Contents.
3. About InterNIC Information Services/
4. InterNIC Store/
5. Getting Started on the Internet/
6. Internet Information for Everybody/
7. Just for NICs/
8. NSFNET, NREN, National Information Infrastructure Information/
9. Search InfoSource by providing Keyword <?>

Note: Mail servers are also available. Send a "help" message to `list-serv@is.internic.net` or to `mailserv@ds.internic.net` (the holdings and services are not the same).

Title: New-List
Resource Type: Mailing List

This is where publicly accessible mailing lists are announced. The contents of this mailing list are eventually included in lists of mailing lists (see Chapter 5). If you want to know about new mailing lists as they are announced to the world, subscribe to NEW-LIST.

A weekly "search digest" is a forum for people who are looking for a list that deals with a particular topic.

Primary/authoritative source: `New-list@vm1.nodak.edu` or
`new-list@ndsuvm1.bitnet`
Instructions for access: To subscribe, send a message of this form to list-serv@vm1.nodak.edu or listserv@ndsuvm1.bitnet `subscribe new-list Your Name`
Additional sources/methods: Monthly archives are available from LISTSERV. Send the command `index new-list` to `listserv@vm1.nodak.edu` or `list-serv@ndsuvm1.bitnet`

Content sample:

COUNCIL on   LISTSERV@SJSUVM1.BITNET
        or   LISTSERV@SJSUVM1.SJSU.EDU

   Global Council Forum—Moving Beyond the Nation-State

   COUNCIL has been created to provide an international computer forum for the discussion of the creation of a global council. It premise is that the world reality has moved beyond the nation-state, yet the world order still relies on this fragmentary concept and structure. The proposal is for the creation of a small, non-power-holding, non-bureaucratic council in East Africa, the birthplace of humanity, in the foreseeable future. Seeking voices from outside North America for discussion. To spur exploration of this issue, the list owner will post a short essay at least once a week, by 0900 GMT Wednesdays.

Note: European subscribers should use the European peer address for the list. The content is exactly the same, but the origination point is in Europe rather than North America. The address for this LISTSERV is `listserv@irlearn.ucd.ie` or `list-serv@irlearn.bitnet` (the mailing list name and subscription procedures are exactly the same).

Title: news.*
Resource Type: Usenet Hierarchy

The `news.` hierarchy contains much of interest. Some of the newsgroups are for discussion, others are for announcements only. Every Usenet reader should read `news.announce.important`. The other newsgroups in this hierarchy include information on the current status of Usenet and the Internet in general, as well as discussions on their futures.

Authors: Many

Primary/authoritative source: Usenet newsgroups
Instructions for access: Read the newsgroups.
Additional sources/methods: Many newsgroups are archived. Use Archie to identify the archive site closest to you.

Copyright restriction: Most materials may be freely distributed.

Experience level: Varies with newsgroup
Target audience: Varies with newsgroup

Current newsgroups:

> news.admin
> news.admin.misc
> news.admin.policy
> news.admin.technical
> news.announce.conferences
> news.announce.important
> news.announce.newgroups
> news.announce.newusers
> news.answers
> news.config
> news.future
> news.groups
> news.lists
> news.lists.ps-maps
> news.misc
> news.newsites
> news.newusers.questions
> news.software.anu-news
> news.software.b
> news.software.nn
> news.software.nntp
> news.software.notes
> news.software.readers
> news.sysadmin

Title: Networked Information Retrieval (NIR)
Resource Type: Mailing List

"The NIR Working Group intends to increase the useful base of information about networked information retrieval (NIR) tools, their developers, interested organizations, and other activities that relate to the production, dissemination, and support of NIR tools, to produce documentation that will enable user services organizations to provide better support for NIR tools, to develop materials that will assist the support and training of end users and to evolve in the future as necessary to meet and anticipate changes in the field (i.e., NIR tools, protocols, network topology, etc.)" (from `mailbase.ac.uk:/pub/nir/nir.charter`).

Primary/authoritative source: mailbase@mailbase.ac.uk
Instructions for access: To subscribe send a message of the form `subscribe nir first-name last-name`
Additional sources/methods: Archives and other files are available via anonymous FTP to `mailbase.ac.uk`

Experience level: Not for general questions about the Internet. Discussion is aimed at experienced network users.

Notes: The NIR group has produced and will continue to produce NIR Status Reports. A March 1993 report is available as `mailbase.ac.uk:/pub/nir/nir.status.report`. This report is useful to general audiences.

Title: Network Information Services
Resource Type: Mailing list

This list is intended as a central announcement point for announcements of networked information services. It is one of the services of the InterNIC (see pages 125–127).

Primary/authoritative source: `Nis@is.internic.net`
Instructions for access: to subscribe send a message of this form to `listserv@is.internic.net: subscribe nis Your Name`

Content sample:

NAVNEWS EXTRAS:

   The following documents are now available by electronic mail:
   — The complete text of the Navy's updated sexual harassment policy, SECNAVINST 5300.26B (see article NNS20 in NAVNEWS issue 003/93 dated 12 Jan 93).
   — An updated fact sheet on U. S. Navy forces participating in Operation Southern Watch (see article NNS38 in NAVNEWS issue 005/93 dated 14 Jan 93).
   — The complete text of the Navy Policy Book (see article NNS39 in NAVNEWS issue 005/93 dated 14 Jan 93). This is a lengthy document, emailed in five sections.

— An advance copy of the 1993 schedule for the Blue Angels, which will be included in a forthcoming issue of NAVNEWS.

— The text of an Atlantic Fleet announcement about Navy ships preparing to leave their homeports to support the Coast Guard in rescuing Haitian migrants at sea.

Any of these documents may be requested by sending email to navnews@nctamslant.navy.mil. Please include your complete Internet email address in the text of your request.

Note: This list is not currently archived, so back issues are not available.

Title: RFC and FYI Indexes
Resource Type: List/Bibliography

These are two indexes to RFCs (Requests for Comments) and FYIs (For Your Information). These documents serve as the technical manuals for the Internet. Inside of the documents are the details that system designers adhere to in designing network applications. There are also a number of less technical documents, such as Krol's *Hitchiker's Guide to the Internet* (RFC1118).

Corporate maintainer: Network Information Center (NIC)
Maintainer affiliation/institution: The Defense Data Network
Maintainer E-mail: Nic@nic.ddn.mil
Maintainer postal address: DDN Network Information Center, 14200 Park Meadow Dr., Suite 200, Chantilly, VA 22021
Maintainer telephone number: 1 (800) 365-3642 (U.S. only) or (703) 802-4535

File format: Text
Number of files: Two
Data format: List
File size: rfc-index.txt is 180KB, 4484 lines; fyi-index.txt is 6KB, 127 lines

Primary/authoritative source: `ftp nic.ddn.mil`
Instructions for access: cd rfc; ascii; `get rfc-index.txt` or `get fyi-index.txt`
Additional sources/methods: These files are widely distributed at worldwide FTP sites. A WAIS source exists for rfc-index.txt (and is searchable through many Gopher sites).

Last known revision date: March 1993
Number of revisions to date: As each new RFC or FYI was added
First issue: Unknown
Next planned revision/planned frequency of revision: As new RFCs and FYIs become available

Copyright restriction: None

Sample entry:

1327 Hardcastle-Kille, S. Mapping between X.400(1988) / ISO 10021 and RFC 822. 1992 May; 113 p. (Format: TXT=228599 bytes) (Obsoletes RFC 987, RFC 1026, RFC 1138, RFC 1148; Updates RFC 822)

Notes: A mail server is available at `nic.ddn.mil` for those without direct Internet access. Send a `help` message to `service@nic.ddn.mil` for details.

Internet drafts are discussion papers that often evolve into RFCs. This and other FTP sites carry the full text of Internet drafts, but an index is not available.

Appendix I: Country Codes

This appendix contains two letter country codes. It was generated from a file containing ISO 3166. The full ISO standard includes additional information used with X.500 services.

An Archie search for either `iso3166` or `country-codes` will reveal the site nearest to you with the updated list. This list currently includes a code for every country or independent domain in the world. As new countries emerge, or the political map of the world otherwise changes, the list will change.

Not every country actually has Internet connectivity. Also, some countries (notably the United States) continue to use old-style ARPANet addressing (e.g., with domains that end in `.COM` and `.EDU`, instead of `.US`). Some countries are marked "new." These were added within the past few years. This list includes 232 listings.

Country	Code
AFGHANISTAN	AF
ALBANIA	AL
ALGERIA	DZ
AMERICAN SAMOA	AS
ANDORRA	AD
ANGOLA	AO
ANGUILLA	AI
ANTARCTICA	AQ
ANTIGUA AND BARBUDA	AG
ARGENTINA	AR
ARMENIA	AM new
ARUBA	AW
AUSTRALIA	AU
AUSTRIA	AT
AZERBAIJAN	AZ new
BAHAMAS	BS
BAHRAIN	BH
BANGLADESH	BD
BARBADOS	BB
BELARUS	BY new
BELGIUM	BE
BELIZE	BZ
BENIN	BJ
BERMUDA	BM
BHUTAN	BT
BOLIVIA	BO
BOSNIA HERCEGOVINA	BA new
BOTSWANA	BW
BOUVET ISLAND	BV
BRAZIL	BR

BRITISH INDIAN OCEAN TERRITORY	IO
BRUNEI DARUSSALAM	BN
BULGARIA	BG
BURKINA FASO	BF
BURUNDI	BI
BYELORUSSIAN SSR	BY
CAMBODIA	KH
CAMEROON	CM
CANADA	CA
CAPE VERDE	CV
CAYMAN ISLANDS	KY
CENTRAL AFRICAN REPUBLIC	CF
CHAD	TD
CHILE	CL
CHINA	CN
CHRISTMAS ISLAND	CX
COCOS (KEELING) ISLANDS	CC
COLOMBIA	CO
COMOROS	KM
CONGO	CG
COOK ISLANDS	CK
COSTA RICA	CR
COTE D'IVOIRE	CI
CROATIA (local name: Hrvatska)	HR new
CUBA	CU
CYPRUS	CY
CZECHOSLOVAKIA	CS
DENMARK	DK
DJIBOUTI	DJ
DOMINICA	DM
DOMINICAN REPUBLIC	DO
EAST TIMOR	TP
ECUADOR	EC
EGYPT	EG
EL SALVADOR	SV
EQUATORIAL GUINEA	GQ
ESTONIA	EE new
ETHIOPIA	ET
FALKLAND ISLANDS (MALVINAS)	FK
FAROE ISLANDS	FO
FIJI	FJ
FINLAND	FI
FRANCE	FR
FRENCH GUIANA	GF
FRENCH POLYNESIA	PF
FRENCH SOUTHERN TERRITORIES	TF
GABON	GA

GAMBIA	GM
GEORGIA	GE new
GERMANY	DE
GHANA	GH
GIBRALTAR	GI
GREECE	GR
GREENLAND	GL
GRENADA	GD
GUADELOUPE	GP
GUAM	GU
GUATEMALA	GT
GUINEA	GN
GUINEA-BISSAU	GW
GUYANA	GY
HAITI	HT
HEARD AND MC DONALD ISLANDS	HM
HONDURAS	HN
HONG KONG	HK
HUNGARY	HU
ICELAND	IS
INDIA	IN
INDONESIA	ID
IRAN (ISLAMIC REPUBLIC OF)	IR
IRAQ	IQ
IRELAND	IE
ISRAEL	IL
ITALY	IT
JAMAICA	JM
JAPAN	JP
JORDAN	JO
KAZAKHSTAN	KZ new
KENYA	KE
KIRIBATI	KI
KOREA, DEMOCRATIC PEOPLE'S REPUBLIC OF	KP
KOREA, REPUBLIC OF	KR
KUWAIT	KW
KYRGYZSTAN	KG new
LAO PEOPLE'S DEMOCRATIC REPUBLIC	LA
LATVIA	LV new
LEBANON	LB
LESOTHO	LS
LIBERIA	LR
LIBYAN ARAB JAMAHIRIYA	LY
LIECHTENSTEIN	LI
LITHUANIA	LT new
LUXEMBOURG	LU
MACAU	MO

MADAGASCAR	MG
MALAWI	MW
MALAYSIA	MY
MALDIVES	MV
MALI	ML
MALTA	MT
MARSHALL ISLANDS	MH
MARTINIQUE	MQ
MAURITANIA	MR
MAURITIUS	MU
MEXICO	MX
MICRONESIA	FM
MOLDOVA, REPUBLIC OF	MD new
MONACO	MC
MONGOLIA	MN
MONTSERRAT	MS
MOROCCO	MA
MOZAMBIQUE	MZ
MYANMAR	MM
NAMIBIA	NA
NAURU	NR
NEPAL	NP
NETHERLANDS	NL
NETHERLANDS ANTILLES	AN
NEUTRAL ZONE	NT
NEW CALEDONIA	NC
NEW ZEALAND	NZ
NICARAGUA	NI
NIGER	NE
NIGERIA	NG
NIUE	NU
NORFOLK ISLAND	NF
NORTHERN MARIANA ISLANDS	MP
NORWAY	NO
OMAN	OM
PAKISTAN	PK
PALAU	PW
PANAMA	PA
PAPUA NEW GUINEA	PG
PARAGUAY	PY
PERU	PE
PHILIPPINES	PH
PITCAIRN	PN
POLAND	PL
PORTUGAL	PT
PUERTO RICO	PR
QATAR	QA

REUNION	RE
ROMANIA	RO
RUSSIAN FEDERATION	RU new
RWANDA	RW
SAINT KITTS AND NEVIS	KN
SAINT LUCIA	LC
SAINT VINCENT AND THE GRENADINES	VC
SAMOA	WS
SAN MARINO	SM
SAO TOME AND PRINCIPE	ST
SAUDI ARABIA	SA
SENEGAL	SN
SEYCHELLES	SC
SIERRA LEONE	SL
SINGAPORE	SG
SLOVENIA	SI new
SOLOMON ISLANDS	SB
SOMALIA	SO
SOUTH AFRICA	ZA
SPAIN	ES
SRI LANKA	LK
ST. HELENA	SH
ST. PIERRE AND MIQUELON	PM
SUDAN	SD
SURINAME	SR
SVALBARD AND JAN MAYEN ISLANDS	SJ
SWAZILAND	SZ
SWEDEN	SE
SWITZERLAND	CH
SYRIAN ARAB REPUBLIC	SY
TAIWAN, PROVINCE OF CHINA	TW
TAJIKISTAN	TJ new
TANZANIA, UNITED REPUBLIC OF	TZ
THAILAND	TH
TOGO	TG
TOKELAU	TK
TONGA	TO
TRINIDAD AND TOBAGO	TT
TUNISIA	TN
TURKEY	TR
TURKMENISTAN	TM new
TURKS AND CAICOS ISLANDS	TC
TUVALU	TV
UGANDA	UG
UKRAINIAN SSR	UA
UNITED ARAB EMIRATES	AE
UNITED KINGDOM	GB

UNITED STATES	US
UNITED STATES MINOR OUTLYING ISLANDS	UM
URUGUAY	UY
USSR	SU
UZBEKISTAN	UZ new
VANUATU	VU
VATICAN CITY STATE (HOLY SEE)	VA
VENEZUELA	VE
VIET NAM	VN
VIRGIN ISLANDS (BRITISH)	VG
VIRGIN ISLANDS (U.S.)	VI
WALLIS AND FUTUNA ISLANDS	WF
WESTERN SAHARA	EH
YEMEN, REPUBLIC OF	YE
YUGOSLAVIA	YU
ZAIRE	ZR
ZAMBIA	ZM
ZIMBABWE	ZW

Appendix II: FTP Mail Service

An FTP mail server is available. It has the E-mail address `bitftp@pucc.bitnet` or `bitftp@pucc.princeton.edu`.

This server is for the use of people who do not have access to FTP on their system. In order to get started, send a help message to one of the email addresses above. BITFTP can not connect to all Internet hosts, and there will be a delay before your data are delivered. From the help output:

BITFTP — Princeton BITNET FTP Server

BITFTP provides a mail interface to the FTP command supplied by the IBM TCP/IP for VM product ("FAL") running on the Princeton University VM/CMS system, to allow BIT-NET/NetNorth/EARN users to ftp files from sites on the Internet.

To use BITFTP, send mail containing your FTP commands to BITFTP@PUCC (or to BITFTP@pucc.Princeton.EDU).

The first command to BITFTP must be "FTP", "HELP", "VMS", or "FTPLIST". Use "HELP" to request a current copy of this help file. Use "VMS" to request a collection of tips provided by BITFTP users on how to handle binary files from BITFTP on VMS systems. Use "FTPLIST" to obtain a list of some of the hosts that allow anonymous FTP. (Note that there is no guarantee that BITFTP can access all the hosts in that list.)

Notes: This service should not be used by anyone who has regular FTP access.

Another FTP mailservice used to exist at `ftpmail@decwrl.dec.com`. However, that service has evidently been discontinued or moved.

Appendix III: Countries with Searchable X.500 Gateways

This is the listing of countries accessible through the Gopher to X.500 gateway. Not every network node in every country is accessible. See Chapter 5 for further discussion of X.500. You can access the gateway on the Phone Book menu of many Gopher servers.

Austria, Australia, Belgium, Brazil, Canada, Switzerland, Czechoslovakia, Germany, Denmark, Spain, Finland, France, Great Britain, Greece, Hungary, Ireland, Israel, India, Iceland, Italy, Japan, Lithuania, Netherlands, Norway, New Zealand, Poland, Portugal, Sweden, Slovenia, United States of America

Glossary

This is not intended to be a general glossary for networking. Instead, you will find brief definitions for some of the terms which are used in this book.

Archie: A database application for finding locations of files available at FTP sites worldwide.

Asynchroneous communication: Communication which does not involve interaction in real time. E-mail is a form of networked asynchroneous communication. Postal letters are non-Internet forms of asynchroneous communication.

Bitnet: The "Because it's There" or "Because it's Time" network. This is a store-and-forward network based on an IBM product called "RSCS" (the Remote Spooling and Console System). Bitnet may be used for email, asynchronous file transfer, and line messaging. Internet and Bitnet users can generally send email to each other without any special knowledge of gateways.

CMC: Computer-Mediated Communication, an umbrella term used to refer to the many different ways by which people can communicate using computer networks.

Computer-Mediated Communication: see CMC.

Cyberspace: In science fiction, "cyberspace" refers to the future of the Internet and the global communication matrix, where business and communication takes place in this "consensual hallucination" (cf. William Gibson's *Neuromancer,* 1984). It is used today to refer generally to the Internet and people, data, and resources who make it up.

Electronic mail, or e-mail, or email: The asynchroneous exchange of messages between people with computer networks as a medium.

Electronic text, or etext, or e-text: A book or other text stored on a computer. These are intended for reading by humans, and therefore must be stored in well-known formats. Some etexts exist as regular printed books, others are produced first as etexts.

FAQ (Frequently Asked Question): A regular posting to a Usenet newsgroup or mailing list which lists questions commonly asked with their answers.

FTP: see File Transfer Protocol.

File Transfer Protocol: A method for the synchronous copying of files over Internet.

GIF: Graphics Interchange Format. Files ending in .gif store encoded graphical images and may be viewed with programs that understand GIF. GIF is one of the more popular graphics standards, and is very prevalant at anonymous FTP sites and newsgroups which transmit pictures.

Gateway: A computer that is attached to more than one network and can transfer data between the networks. A common example is a Bitnet-to-Internet gateway which may be used to faciliate the exchange of email between people on Bitnet and the Internet.

Gopher: Internet protocol and set of applications used to navigate network resources with a simple menu-driven interface, without regard for the physical location of the resources.

IP address: A numeric address usually of the form aaa.bbb.ccc.ddd. Every computer attached to the Internet must have a unique IP address, which is used to exchange messages with other computers. Most Internet nodes have an alphanumeric equivalent of their IP address.

IP: The Internet Protocol. This is the fundamental method by which computers connected to the Internet exchange messages. Other protocols are layered on IP for particular applications, for example, "SMTP" (the Simple Mail Transport Protocol) is used for the exchange of e-mail.

Line messaging: Bitnet users may send single-line messages to users or commands to Bitnet nodes. On CMS, this is done with the TELL command. On VMS is is done with `send/remote` or `send/command`.

OPAC: The Online Public Access Catalog, or electronic card catalog, of a library.

Supercomputer: The most powerful type of computer currently available. These are able to perform up to one billion calculations per second. Because of their cost, supercomputers are frequently located centrally in supercomputer centers for access by academics and corporations.

Surfing: Term used to refer to the practice of exploring Internet resources (see also page 34).

Synchroneous communication: Communication that involves all parties' involvement at the same time. Interactive messaging is a form of networked synchroneous communication. The telephone is one method for synchroneous communication in the non-Internet world.

Telnet: A method for enabling synchroneous access to remote computers over the Internet.

WAIS: Wide Area Information Servers, an application of the Z39.50 protocol for remote access to databases across the Internet.

WHOIS: A service for looking up persons at particular institutions. Originally developed by the U.S. Department of Defense, the software for WHOIS is available free of charge to anyone interested in maintaining their own WHOIS database.

Wide Area Information Server: see WAIS.

X.500: A standard for Internet directory services. Enables routing of mail and white-pages inquiries with mnemonic codes, instead of combinations of usernames and IP addresses.

Z39.50: A protocol for remote access to databases over the Internet (see WAIS). This will soon be used to provide transparent access to library databases worldwide.

Index by Resource Type

Index by Internet Address

Index by Author, Maintainer, or Supplier

Subject Index